PRENTICE HALL
LITERATURE

PENGUIN EDITION

Teaching Resources

Unit 6
Themes in the Oral Tradition

Grade Seven

PEARSON

Prentice
Hall

Upper Saddle River, New Jersey
Boston, Massachusetts

CUR
63
PH
7
2007
TR
V.6

ISBN 0-13-190788-3

1 2 3 4 5 6 7 8 9 10   09 08 07 06 05

BD

Contents

Part 1 Cause and Effect

"Grasshopper Logic," "The Other Frog Prince," and "duckbilled platypus vs. beefsnakstik®" by Jon Scieszka and Lane Smith

"Icarus and Daedalus" by Josephine Preston Peabody

"Demeter and Persephone" by Anne Terry White

"Tenochtitlan: Inside the Aztec Capital" by Jacqueline Dineen

"Popocatepetl and Ixtlaccihuatl" by Juliet Piggott Wood

"Perseus" by Alice Low

"Percy-Us Brings the Gawgon's Head" by Lloyd Alexander

Writing Workshop: Letter—Business Letter

Writing Workshop: Integrating Grammar Skills

Benchmark Test 11

Part 2 Comparison and Contrast

"All Stories Are Anansi's" by Harold Courlander

"The Fox Outwits the Crow" by William Cleary

"The Fox and the Crow" by Aesop

"Grasshopper Logic," "The Other Frog Prince," and "duckbilled platypus vs. beefsnakstik®" by Jon Scieszka and Lane Smith

Vocabulary Warm-up Word Lists

Study these words from the selections. Then, complete the activities that follow.

Word List A

bragged [BRAGD] *v.* boasted
  The proud grandmother <u>bragged</u> about her talented grandchildren.

fur [FUR] *n.* the soft, thick hair covering many mammals
  The rabbit's <u>fur</u> was white with black spots.

hopped [HAHPT] *v.* jumped in a short, springing motion
  At the zoo, the kangaroo <u>hopped</u> over to its shelter.

moral [MAWR uhl] *v.* a lesson that is taught by a story, situation, or fable
  The <u>moral</u> of the story is to always tell the truth.

pathetic [puh THET ik] *adj.* causing feelings of pity
  The weak, hungry kittens were a <u>pathetic</u> sight.

plenty [PLEN tee] *n.* a lot of something
  We have <u>plenty</u> of milk and cheese in the refrigerator.

promptly [PRAHMPT lee] *adv.* quickly or without delay
  Billy <u>promptly</u> reported to work at seven in the morning.

wiped [WYPD] *v.* rubbed with something in order to clean something else
  We <u>wiped</u> the grime off the windshield wipers of the car.

Word List B

history [HIS tuh ree] *n.* a class on recorded past events
  In <u>history</u>, we are learning about the Revolutionary War.

logic [LAHJ ik] *n.* a way of reasoning
  Mary used faulty <u>logic</u> to figure out how to read the map.

mammals [MAM uhlz] *n.* warm-blooded animals that have hair and nurse their young
  Camels are <u>mammals</u> that live in the desert.

princess [PRIN ses] *n.* the daughter of a king or queen
  The <u>princess</u> wore a beautiful gown to the ball.

production [pruh DUK shuhn] *n.* a work produced on the stage
  The Broadway <u>production</u> of the musical *Oklahoma* was a big success.

rewrite [ree RYT] *v.* to write again, often in a new form or using new words
  For English class, we must choose a story and <u>rewrite</u> the ending.

spell [SPEL] *n.* a charm or words that have magical power
  The good queen arrived and broke the magic <u>spell</u>.

wicked [WIK id] *adj.* evil, morally bad or wrong
  In the fairy tale, a <u>wicked</u> king ruled the land.

Name _____ Date _____

"Grasshopper Logic," "The Other Frog Prince," and "duckbilled platypus vs. beefsnakstik®" by Jon Scieszka and Lane Smith
Vocabulary Warm-up Exercises

Exercise A *Fill in each blank in the paragraph below with an appropriate word from Word List A. Use each word only once.*

Mark proudly [1] _____ to Al that he could beat him in a long bicycle race. Mark knew his fancy bike with [2] _____ of gears and a soft seat covered with [3] _____ could go fast. Mark thought that Al's bike was a [4] _____ piece of junk compared with his own bicycle. Al realized his bike was a simple one, but he was used to riding long distances on it. He agreed to race and both boys [5] _____ on their bicycles. Mark [6] _____ took the lead, but then mud splashed up and clogged his gears. He [7] _____ them off the best he could, but Al passed him and won the race. The [8] _____ of the story is that sometimes simple is best!

Exercise B *Revise each sentence so that the underlined vocabulary word is used in a way that makes sense. Be sure to keep the vocabulary word in your revision.*

Example: In <u>history</u>, we are learning many interesting facts about math equations.
In <u>history</u>, we are learning many interesting facts about past events.

1. When the <u>princess</u> arrived, the photographers didn't want to take her picture.
   _____

2. <u>Mammals</u>, such as horses and dogs, are cold-blooded animals.
   _____

3. The <u>wicked</u> boss always treated his employees fairly.
   _____

4. The <u>logic</u> of the witches' <u>spell</u> was easy to comprehend.
   _____

5. If you <u>rewrite</u> your assignment, it is a first draft of your work.
   _____

6. The <u>production</u> of the play is meant to be seen on film.
   _____

2

Name _____ Date _____

"Grasshopper Logic," "The Other Frog Prince," and "duckbilled platypus vs. beefsnakstik®" by Jon Scieszka and Lane Smith
Reading Warm-up A

Read the following passage. Pay special attention to the underlined words. Then, read it again, and complete the activities. Use a separate sheet of paper for your written answers.

Here is a very old fable from a storyteller named Aesop. It is the tale of "The Ant and the Grasshopper."

One hot day, a merry grasshopper sat in the shade sipping a cool drink and singing happily. He loved his idle life. Sometimes, as he sang a song, he also <u>hopped</u> about, doing a dance to celebrate the easy life of summer.

As the grasshopper played, a small ant crawled by. The ant was sweating and working very hard. The tiny insect was busily dragging an entire ear of corn down the road. "Stop a moment and rest," said the grasshopper to the ant. "It is a hot day. Why are you toiling away?" The ant <u>wiped</u> the sweat from his brow. He said, "A cold winter is coming. You had better get busy storing up some food for the days ahead." The grasshopper laughed and said, "Look around you. There is <u>plenty</u> to eat." The ant shook his head and continued on his way.

The grasshopper awoke from a pleasant nap only to find the ant dragging a huge chunk of rabbit <u>fur</u> down the road. "What have you there?" asked the grasshopper. "I found this fur in an old rabbit's nest," said the ant. "It will help me keep warm during the cold days of winter. You should go get some, too." The grasshopper said he saw no need for that. "My comfortable hammock and shady home are just perfect," he <u>bragged</u>. The ant shook his head and <u>promptly</u> continued on his way.

The warm days of summer gave way to fall. The cool fall days turned to cold, winter ones. The <u>pathetic</u> grasshopper shivered in the cold. He could find no food anywhere. The ant, however, was cozy, warm, and well fed in his house beneath the frozen ground.

<u>Moral</u>: Plan ahead for the days of necessity.

1. Circle the words that tell what the grasshopper did as he <u>hopped</u> about. Define *hopped*.

2. Circle the words that tell what the ant <u>wiped</u>. Use *wiped* in a sentence.

3. Underline the words that tell of what the grasshopper said there was <u>plenty</u>. What things do you think there are *plenty* of?

4. Circle the words that tell why the ant wanted the rabbit <u>fur</u>. What is *fur*?

5. Underline the words that tell what the grasshopper <u>bragged</u> about. Use *bragged* in a sentence.

6. Circle the words that tell what the ant <u>promptly</u> did. What have you ever done *promptly*?

7. Underline the words that describe more about why the grasshopper was <u>pathetic</u>. Use *pathetic* in a sentence.

8. Underline the words that tell the <u>moral</u> of the story. What is a *moral*?

"Grasshopper Logic," "The Other Frog Prince," and "duckbilled platypus vs. beefsnakstik®" by Jon Scieszka and Lane Smith
Reading Warm-up B

Read the following passage. Pay special attention to the underlined words. Then, read it again, and complete the activities. Use a separate sheet of paper for your written answers.

Are you familiar with fairy tales and legends? As little children, we often hear and read make-believe stories that have been handed down through time. These fantastic stories may have human characters in them. There may be a <u>princess</u> and a <u>wicked</u> witch; there may be a wizard who can cast a magic <u>spell</u>. Yet other fairy tales and folktales have animal characters. These animals talk and have other human traits. The Br'er Rabbit stories of African-Americans are an example of these. The main characters are <u>mammals</u>, such as a rabbit and a fox. In these tales, the two always try to outsmart each other.

Many people have studied fairy tales and legends from around the world. In presenting this topic's <u>history</u>, these scholars have found that many similar stories come from different parts of the world. People have tried to figure out how this occurred. Some believed that the tales spread from various parts of the world as explorers and conquerors moved from place to place. Perhaps their travels brought and mixed the tales of various cultures. The <u>logic</u> of this theory, however, has never been proved.

Other scholars believe that people throughout the world, despite having different cultures, religions, and histories, are alike. They all have the same basic need to express themselves through storytelling. These scholars believe the stories that grow out of this need show how much all people have in common.

Even today, many old stories that are based on legends and folktales are retold. Authors <u>rewrite</u> them and present them as novels and movies. The next time you see a <u>production</u> of a play that is based on a fairy tale or legend, enjoy it—and marvel at the idea that a story from long ago is still a part of today's culture.

1. Underline the words that tell where a character such as a <u>princess</u> may be found. What is a *princess*?

2. Circle the word that <u>wicked</u> modifies. Use *wicked* in a sentence.

3. Circle the words in the story that tell who might cast a magic <u>spell</u>. Who else might cast a *spell*?

4. Underline the words that give two examples of <u>mammals</u> that are main characters. Name a few other kinds of *mammals*.

5. Underline what scholars who have presented this topic's <u>history</u> have found. Define *history*.

6. Circle the words that tell whether the <u>logic</u> of the theory has or has not been proved. Use *logic* in a sentence.

7. Circle the words that tell what authors sometimes <u>rewrite</u>. Tell about something you have had to *rewrite* for a class project, or just for fun.

8. Underline the words that tell more about what a <u>production</u> is. Name a stage *production* that you have seen or would like to see.

Name _____ Date _____

Jon Scieszka
Listening and Viewing

Segment 1: Meet Jon Scieszka
- How did Jon Scieszka choose his audience? Scieszka reads all different types of literature.
- How do you think this helps him come up with writing ideas?

_____

_____

_____

_____

Segment 2: Themes in the Oral Tradition
- Why is Jon Scieszka "amazed" by fairy tales, myths, and legends?
- Why do you think that the retelling of these stories over time is important?

_____

_____

_____

_____

Segment 3: The Writing Process
- Who is Lane Smith, and how is he involved in Jon Scieszka's writing process?
- Why are illustrations important in fairy tales, myths, and fables like the stories that Jon Scieszka writes?

_____

_____

_____

_____

Segment 4: The Rewards of Writing
- Why is being a writer rewarding to Jon Scieszka?
- Why do you think that reading is a valuable activity for young people in today's age of technology?

_____

_____

_____

_____

Learning About the Oral Tradition

The sharing of stories, cultures, and ideas by word of mouth is called the **oral tradition.** Here are common elements of the oral tradition.

- The **theme** is a central idea, message, or insight that a story reveals.
- A **moral** is a lesson about life that is taught by a story.
- **Heroes** and **heroines** are larger-than-life figures whose virtues and deeds are often celebrated in stories from the oral tradition.
- **Storytelling** calls on the talents and personality of the teller to bring the narrative to life. Storytelling techniques include **hyperbole,** or the use of exaggeration or overstatement, and **personification,** the giving of human characteristics to a non-human subject.

Many stories have been written down for readers. Categories of stories in the oral tradition that have been committed to paper include the following.

- **Myths** are ancient tales that describe the actions of gods, goddesses, and the heroes who interact with them.
- **Legends** are traditional stories about the past. They are based on real-life events or people, but they are more fiction than fact.
- **Folk tales** tell about ordinary people. These stories reveal the traditions and values of a culture and teach a lesson about life.
- **Tall tales** are folk tales that contain hyperbole.
- **Fables** are brief animal stories that contain personification. Fables often end with a moral or lesson.
- **Epics** are long narrative poems about a hero who engages in a dangerous journey.

A. DIRECTIONS: *The following items are elements of stories in the oral tradition. Decide which of the two terms matches the preceding description. Underline your choice.*

1. A woman spins cloth out of gold.   hyperbole   personification
2. The god Apollo drives his chariot across the sky.   myth   legend
3. Baseball great Babe Ruth hits the ball into another state.   fable   legend
4. The sun refuses to shine on an evil character's birthday.   personification   theme
5. It is best to be prepared.   moral   hero

B. DIRECTIONS: *On the lines below, write a plot summary for an original fable. Include one or more animal characters, and include an example of personification. End your fable with a moral. Use a separate sheet of paper if more space is needed.*

_____

_____

_____

Name _____ Date _____

Model Selection: The Oral Tradition

Jon Scieszka entertains readers with his comical versions of traditional **fairy tales** and **fables. Fables** are brief animal stories that contain personification. Fables often end with a moral or lesson. These three short selections are humorous examples of stories in the **oral tradition**—the sharing of stories, cultures, and ideas by word of mouth. Elements of the oral tradition include the following.

- The **theme** is a central idea, message, or insight that a story reveals.
- A **moral** is a lesson about life that is taught by a story. An example of a moral is "Hard work leads to success."
- **Hyperbole** is a deliberate exaggeration or overstatement. It is often used to create humor. For example, a man might be as strong as an ox.
- **Personification** is the granting of human characteristics to a nonhuman subject. This would include a talking fox or an angry tree.

A. DIRECTIONS: *Answer the following questions.*

1. Give an example of hyperbole from "Grasshopper Logic." Tell why it is a hyperbole.

   _____

   _____

2. How does the ending of "The Other Frog Prince" differ from the ending of the traditional "Frog Prince" fairy tale?

   _____

   _____

3. What types of characters are in "duckbilled platypus vs. beefsnakstik®," and in what specific ways are they examples of personification?

   _____

   _____

B. DIRECTIONS: *On the lines below, describe the specific ways in which the grasshopper and his mother talk and act like humans.*

_____

_____

_____

_____

_____

7

"Grasshopper Logic," "The Other Frog Prince,"
and "duckbilled platypus vs. beefsnakstik®" by Jon Scieszka and Lane Smith
Selection Test A

Learning About the Oral Tradition *Identify the letter of the choice that best answers the question.*

____ 1. Which term names the central idea or message that a story reveals?
   A. theme
   B. legend
   C. personification
   D. myth

____ 2. Which term names a lesson about life that is taught by a story?
   A. myth
   B. legend
   C. moral
   D. conflict

____ 3. Which storytelling technique allows an animal to talk and act like a human?
   A. personification
   B. metaphor
   C. hyperbole
   D. onomatopoeia

____ 4. Which of the following is an example of hyperbole?
   A. a story about ancient gods
   B. a bird that builds a cozy nest
   C. a man who solves a big problem
   D. a man who is as tall as a tree

____ 5. Which statement about stories that are part of the oral tradition is true?
   A. All of these stories appear in books.
   B. Each one features a talking animal that learns an important lesson about life.
   C. Each one has been passed down by word of mouth.
   D. Each one features a magical or evil character, such as a wicked witch.

Critical Reading

___ 6. In "Grasshopper Logic," what did Grasshopper want to do right after school?
   A. go out with his friends
   B. finish his homework
   C. rewrite some myths
   D. spend time with his mother

___ 7. What hyperbole, or exaggeration, occurs in "Grasshopper Logic"?
   A. Grasshopper's height
   B. Grasshopper's homework assignment
   C. Mom Grasshopper's angry words
   D. Grasshopper's friends

___ 8. In "The Other Frog Prince," why does the frog speak to the princess?
   A. He wants to become a prince.
   B. He thinks she is very beautiful.
   C. He is lost and needs directions.
   D. He is really a wicked witch in disguise.

___ 9. Why does the princess help the frog?
   A. He promises her money.
   B. She wants to trick him.
   C. She feels sorry for him.
   D. He is covered with slime.

___ 10. What happens after the princess kisses the frog in "The Other Frog Prince"?
   A. They live happily ever after.
   B. He turns into a wicked witch.
   C. He turns into a handsome prince and rewards her with a necklace.
   D. He says that he was only kidding and jumps back into the pond.

___ 11. Which statement about "duckbilled platypus vs. beefsnakstik®" is true?
   A. It is a fable.
   B. It is a myth.
   C. It is a folk tale.
   D. It is a legend.

Name _____ Date _____

___ 12. What are Platypus and BeefSnakStik® doing during this story?
   A. competing in a race
   B. bragging about their features
   C. listening to a story
   D. trying to improve themselves

___ 13. According to this story, what is true about BeefSnakStik®?
   A. He has webbed feet.
   B. He is a hyperbole.
   C. He is under the spell of a witch.
   D. He contains many food additives.

___ 14. The platypus brags and the frog plays a trick on the princess. What type of storytelling technique do these characters exemplify?
   A. hyperbole
   B. metaphor
   C. moral
   D. personification

___ 15. Which statement is true about "Grasshopper Logic," "The Other Frog Prince," and "duckbilled platypus vs. beefsnakstik®"?
   A. Two are fables, and one is a folk tale.
   B. Two are legends, and one is a fable.
   C. All three are myths.
   D. All three are folk tales.

Essay

16. In a brief essay, describe how you think the princess feels at the end of "The Other Frog Prince." What did the princess expect would happen? Did the ending differ from her expectations?

17. What characteristics of the oral tradition can be found in "Grasshopper Logic"? In a brief essay, describe these characteristics and techniques using examples from the story. Think about what category the story falls under. Does the story teach a lesson or moral? If so, what is it?

"Grasshopper Logic," "The Other Frog Prince," and "duckbilled platypus vs. beefsnakstik®" by Jon Scieszka and Lane Smith

Selection Test B

Learning About the Oral Tradition *Identify the letter of the choice that best completes the statement or answers the question.*

____ 1. An ancient tale about Ares, the god of war, is an example of a
    A. fable.
    B. folk tale.
    C. legend.
    D. myth.

____ 2. Which statement is true about every story's <u>theme</u>?
    A. It is a creative explanation, such as "why leopards have spots."
    B. It teaches a lesson, such as "Always tell the truth."
    C. It is a central idea, message, or insight about life.
    D. It is an exaggeration, often used to add humor to the story.

____ 3. A dog who wears a suit and works in an office is an example of
    A. personification.
    B. moral.
    C. hyperbole.
    D. theme.

____ 4. This type of literature is called the <u>oral</u> <u>tradition</u> because it includes stories that
    A. are about animals.
    B. teach lessons about traditional values.
    C. have been passed down through word of mouth.
    D. often include magical or evil characters.

____ 5. The lesson about life that is taught by a story is called the
    A. hyperbole.
    B. moral.
    C. legend.
    D. instruction.

____ 6. Which is the BEST definition of a <u>tall</u> <u>tale</u>?
    A. a myth that contains personification
    B. a legend that features an evil character
    C. a folk tale that has animal characters
    D. a folk tale that contains hyperbole

Critical Reading

____ 7. In "Grasshopper Logic," Grasshopper tells his mother that he has
    A. a large assignment due tomorrow.
    B. a small assignment due tomorrow.
    C. no school tomorrow.
    D. no homework due tomorrow.

____ 8. Grasshopper's mother got upset because
   A. Grasshopper was late for dinner.
   B. Grasshopper lost his backpack.
   C. Grasshopper did a sloppy and incomplete job on his homework.
   D. Grasshopper's homework assignment was very large.

____ 9. When Grasshopper's mom asks him how long he has known about the assignment, he says,
   A. "I don't know."
   B. "Since last week."
   C. "Since this morning."
   D. "I can't remember."

____ 10. "The Other Frog Prince" is an example of a
   A. legend.
   B. epic.
   C. myth.
   D. fable.

____ 11. When the frog speaks to the princess in "The Other Frog Prince," she starts to jump up and run because
   A. he is ugly and covered with warts.
   B. she is frightened by the witch.
   C. she is very surprised that a frog can speak.
   D. she has a feeling that he will try to trick her.

____ 12. In "The Other Frog Prince," the princess feels sorry for the frog because
   A. she knows how wicked the evil witch is.
   B. he speaks in such a sad and pathetic voice.
   C. he is covered with frog slime.
   D. most frogs have very lonely lives.

____ 13. The humor at the end of "The Other Frog Prince" is caused by
   A. the unexpected ending, in which the frog says that he was only kidding.
   B. the unexpected ending, in which the frog turns into an ugly prince.
   C. the joke that the princess plays on the frog.
   D. the funny joke that the princess tells.

____ 14. The story "duckbilled platypus vs. beefsnakstik®" is an example of a
   A. legend.
   B. fable.
   C. myth.
   D. hyperbole.

____ 15. The realistic elements in "duckbilled platypus vs. beefsnakstik®" involve
   A. the facts and details about what each character has or can do.
   B. the voices of the characters.
   C. the way in which the characters argue and reason with each other.
   D. the proud attitude of the platypus.

____ 16. Which statement *best* sums up the lesson of "duckbilled platypus vs. beefsnakstik®"?
  A. The platypus is a very strange animal.
  B. BeefSnakStik® is a healthy and delicious snack food.
  C. Animals must be careful regarding what they eat.
  D. Do not be too proud about how "special" you are.

____ 17. Which statement *best* describes BeefSnakStik®'s attitude toward the platypus?
  A. He is not impressed with what the platypus says about himself.
  B. He thinks that the platypus is really weird.
  C. He thinks that the platypus is under the spell of a witch.
  D. He knows that the platypus has more important features than he has himself.

____ 18. Which is the *best* example of personification from Scieszka's tales?
  A. a sympathetic princess who is easily fooled
  B. a platypus who brags
  C. a frog who jumps out of the water
  D. a beefsnakstik® that contains soy protein concentrate

____ 19. Which character from Scieszka's tales has the *best* reason to feel surprised and tricked at the end of the story?
  A. the platypus
  B. the grasshopper
  C. the princess
  D. the beefsnakstik®

Essay

20. Write a summary of "The Other Frog Prince" from the princess's point of view. Make sure that you show her thoughts and feelings about the frog and what takes place in the story.

21. If "Grasshopper Logic" were to continue, what do you think would happen next? How will Mom Grasshopper react? Will Grasshopper learn his lesson? Describe your prediction in a brief essay and support it with details from the story.

22. In a brief essay, describe the moral of "The Other Frog Prince." Use details from the story to support your response.

Unit 6: Themes in Oral Tradition
Part 1 Concept Map

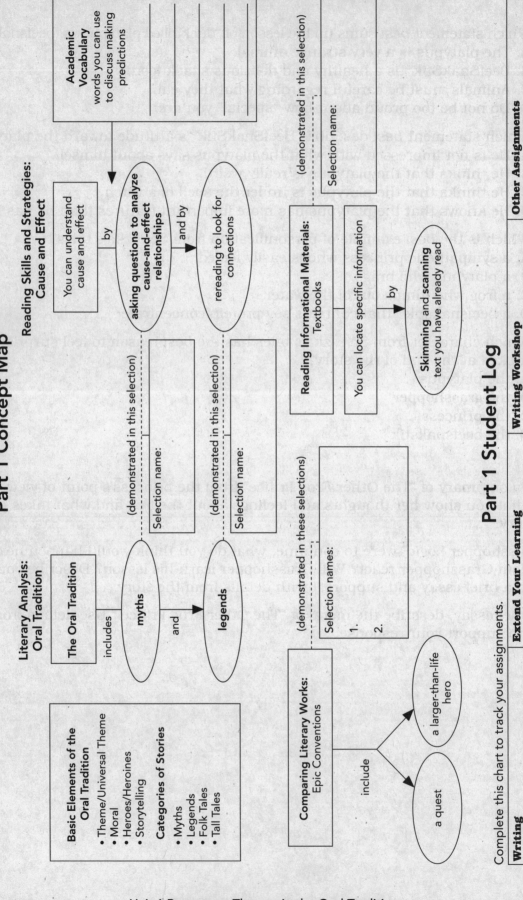

Academic Vocabulary
words you can use to discuss making predictions

_____
_____
_____
_____

Reading Skills and Strategies: Cause and Effect

You can understand cause and effect

→ by → **asking questions to analyze cause-and-effect relationships** → and by → rereading to look for connections

(demonstrated in this selection)
Selection name: _____

(demonstrated in this selection)
Selection name: _____

(demonstrated in this selection)
Selection name: _____

Reading Informational Materials: Textbooks

You can locate specific information

→ by → **Skimming and scanning text you have already read**

Literary Analysis: Oral Tradition

The Oral Tradition → includes → **myths** → and → **legends**

Basic Elements of the Oral Tradition
• Theme/Universal Theme
• Moral
• Heroes/Heroines
• Storytelling

Categories of Stories
• Myths
• Legends
• Folk Tales
• Tall Tales

Comparing Literary Works: Epic Conventions

include

→ a larger-than-life hero
→ a quest

(demonstrated in these selections)
Selection names:
1. _____
2. _____

Part 1 Student Log

Complete this chart to track your assignments.

Writing	Extend Your Learning	Writing Workshop	Other Assignments

Unit 6: Themes in the Oral Tradition
Part 1 Diagnostic Test 11

MULTIPLE CHOICE

Read the selection. Then, answer the questions that follow.

The historic city center of Amsterdam is composed of narrow streets, unique buildings, and waterways for boats. Instead of palaces, monuments, or churches, the majority of the buildings are homes. They were built for the wealthy people who were the backbone of Amsterdam.

You can take a leisurely bicycle tour to see the most outstanding homes in the city center. You will notice that most Amsterdam homes are very narrow and attached to one another. The crowded streets of old Amsterdam must have been vibrant. Among the oldest buildings you will see are the two remaining wooden houses in the city center. Two citywide fires destroyed many wooden structures. The fire of 1452 actually burned down three-quarters of the city!

After the fire, no permanent homes were allowed to have wooden sidewalls. Builders used brick and stone, often carving fancy figures on the outsides of the homes. You can see statues and vases, garlands and scrolls, and symbols of the homeowners' professions.

Some homes have words carved into the walls, such as the names of the houses and the favorite sayings of owners. The tops of the Amsterdam houses—the famous gables, where the walls meet the roof—also have amazing details.

1. What is unusual about the center of the city of Amsterdam?
   A. waterways for boats
   B. palaces
   C. monuments
   D. bicycle trails

2. What might you normally expect to find in the center of an old city like Amsterdam?
   A. sports arenas and shopping malls
   B. factories
   C. businesses
   D. palaces and monuments

3. What kind of buildings actually make up most of the center of Amsterdam?
   A. homes built for the wealthy
   B. palaces for the rulers
   C. churches
   D. boat docks

4. What is unusual about the homes in Amsterdam?
   A. They are especially large and most have boat docks.
   B. They are surrounded by intersecting bicycle trails.
   C. They are very narrow and attached to one another.
   D. Most were built by skilled architects in the early 1400s.

5. Why are wooden sidewalls not allowed in Amsterdam homes?
   A. Wooden sidewalls are too ordinary.
   B. Wooden sidewalls could easily burn.
   C. Wooden homes are not sturdy.
   D. Wooden homes do not last very long.

6. What material was used to make most of Amsterdam's old homes?
   A. granite stone
   B. brick and stone
   C. marble
   D. iron framing

7. What was carved on the outsides of Amsterdam's homes?
   A. famous gables
   B. street addresses
   C. statues and garlands
   D. owners' names

8. The carvings on the homes might give the appearance of which of the following?
   A. lack of decoration inside the home
   B. architects with unusual tastes
   C. the pride of the owners in their homes
   D. the fear of a citywide fire

Read the selection. Then, answer the questions that follow.

Angel Island, looking across San Francisco Bay, was once the first stop for people coming to a new homeland. In the past it was also used to shelter people with contagious illnesses like tuberculosis.

However, the Miwok Indians were the first to enjoy Angel Island. They crossed the bay by boat to hunt and fish on the island. They used the rich resources on the island to fight off hunger. The Miwok never lived there permanently, but they built protective shelters. They would visit the island in good weather, staying as long as they wanted. Then they would return to their small villages on the mainland.

If you visit Angel Island today, you can hike the hilly trails and admire the many beautiful plants and trees. You can still feel the relentless wind as you stand high up on the island, looking out to sea. You might even get to watch sea lions playing on the waves. These are some of the same experiences the Miwok had when they lived on Angel Island. If you are lucky, you might even hear the sounds of their drums and flutes carried across time on the fresh ocean breezes.

9. Angel Island has been used for which of the following?
   A. to keep the Miwok Indians away from the settlers on the mainland
   B. to attract tourists with its many beautiful plants and animals
   C. for residents of San Francisco to use for hiking and bicycling
   D. to keep people with contagious diseases away from others

10. What people were the first to make use of Angel Island?
   A. residents of San Francisco
   B. Miwok Indians
   C. new immigrants to this country
   D. sick people

11. How did the first people get to Angel Island?
   A. They used boats to cross the bay.
   B. They were dropped off by ships.
   C. They rode on barges to croos the bay.
   D. They came up the coast by canoe.

12. What resources attracted the first visitors to Angel Island?
   A. the fish and game animals
   B. the many hiking trails
   C. the good medical care
   D. the beautiful villages and ports

13. Which of the following is true of the Miwok Indians?
   A. They built villages on Angel Island.
   B. They stayed on Angel Island in summer.
   C. They owned Angel Island.
   D. They hunted and fished on Angel Island.

Name _____ Date _____

14. Which of the following made Angel Island their permanent home?
  A. sick people
  B. only the animals
  C. Miwok Indians
  D. settlers from San Francisco

15. What can you find on Angel Island today?
  A. a Miwok Indian village
  B. a fine hospital
  C. hiking trails in the hills
  D. a government Office of Immigration

"Icarus and Daedalus" by Josephine Preston Peabody
Vocabulary Warm-up Word Lists

Study these words from "Icarus and Daedalus." Then, complete the activities that follow.

Word List A

attempt [uh TEMPT] *v.* to try to do something
   Jan was finally successful in her <u>attempt</u> to score a goal.

captive [KAP tiv] *adj.* held prisoner
   The <u>captive</u> soldier was held in a prison camp until after the war.

delay [DEE lay] *n.* a length of waiting time
   The sick woman needed to see a doctor without <u>delay</u>.

fashioned [FASH uhnd] *v.* to have made or shaped something
   The potter <u>fashioned</u> a beautiful vase out of clay.

favor [FAY ver] *n.* an approving or supportive attitude
   Everyone hoped to win the king's <u>favor</u>.

glimpse [GLIMPS] *n.* a brief, quick view
   We caught a <u>glimpse</u> of the president through the window of the train.

liberty [LIB er tee] *n.* freedom
   Americans have the <u>liberty</u> to move around the country.

thirst [thurst] *n.* a longing or strong desire for something
   People who have a <u>thirst</u> for fame are often overachievers.

Word List B

aloft [uh LAWFT] *adj.* up in the air
   The hot air balloon was <u>aloft</u> high above the trees.

architect [AHR ki tekt] *n.* someone who designs buildings
   The <u>architect</u> examined the plans for the new building.

cautions [KAW shuhnz] *n.* words of warning
   Will listened to his mother's <u>cautions</u> about driving too fast.

imprisoned [im PRIZ uhnd] *v.* to put someone in prison; to lock up a person
   The criminal was <u>imprisoned</u> for 20 years to pay for her crime.

overtook [oh ver TOOK] *v.* caught up to someone; came upon suddenly
   The cowboy <u>overtook</u> the runaway bull, and roped it.

quench [KWENCH] *v.* to satisfy
   Drinking a glass of cold lemonade is a great way to <u>quench</u> your thirst.

sustained [suh STAYND] *v.* carried the weight of; supported
   The freight elevator <u>sustained</u> a maximum load of 1,000 pounds.

wavered [WAY verd] *v.* moved back and forth
   The bicycle <u>wavered</u> a few times until the rider found his balance.

"Icarus and Daedalus" by Josephine Preston Peabody
Vocabulary Warm-up Exercises

Exercise A *Fill in each blank in the paragraph below with an appropriate word from Word List A. Use each word only once.*

I caught a [1] _____ of a flash of color beating against the garage window and took a closer look. A hummingbird was [2] _____ inside. In its [3] _____ for freedom, the tiny creature flew repeatedly toward the light and into the window. I had to rescue it without a moment's [4] _____ before it broke its neck. Quickly, I [5] _____ a net out of badminton netting and two fishing poles.

My first [6] _____ to catch the bird was clumsy, but then on the second try it flew right into the net. I released it outside. Although the bird was at [7] _____ to fly away, it paused in midair before my eyes. It seemed just like a monarch bestowing his [8] _____ to show his thanks.

Exercise B *Revise each sentence so that the underlined vocabulary word is used in a logical way.*

Example: As soon as his plane was <u>aloft</u> the pilot put away his flight map.
As soon as his plane was <u>aloft</u>, the pilot took out his flight map.

1. The company hired an <u>architect</u> to design the new phone system.
   _____

2. The <u>imprisoned</u> man enjoyed his freedom.
   _____

3. The customer ordered eggs and bacon to <u>quench</u> his thirst.
   _____

4. Amy listened to her mom's <u>cautions</u> and always wore a straw hat when riding her bike.
   _____

5. The acrobat <u>sustained</u> three other acrobats on his shoulders thanks to his lack of strength.
   _____

6. The athlete lost the race after he <u>overtook</u> the lead runner at the last minute.
   _____

7. When the car wheels <u>wavered</u>, Michael increased the speed.
   _____

"Icarus and Daedalus" by Josephine Preston Peabody
Reading Warm-up A

Read the following passage. Pay special attention to the underlined words. Then, read it again, and complete the activities. Use a separate sheet of paper for your written answers.

Centuries before the Wright Brothers invented the airplane, humans had tried to fly. Every <u>attempt</u> failed, but that did not stop people from trying. Watching birds fly through air gave humans a <u>glimpse</u> of unimaginable freedom. They longed for the <u>liberty</u> of flight.

Then, during the 15th century, a man with a <u>thirst</u> for invention turned his attention to flight. This man with a desire to create new things was Leonardo da Vinci. Like many before him, Leonardo focused on the wings of birds. He designed flying machines with bird-like, flapping wings. None of them ever got off the ground. His ideas were good, but the materials he needed didn't exist.

Then, after a <u>delay</u> of 500 years, Leonardo's theory finally took flight. On December 2, 2003, a man named Angelo D'Arrigo flew a model of Leonardo's flying machine, the *Piuma*, or feather. The event took place in the Italian town where Leonardo was born.

To build the machine, D'Arrigo and his team followed Leonardo's drawings in all ways but one. They <u>fashioned</u> the model out of aluminum tubes and a synthetic fiber. These modern materials made the model about 170 pounds lighter than Leonardo's original machine.

The *Piuma* was tested in a wind tunnel. "At [almost 22 miles] per hour, I took off and flew," said D'Arrigo. "The weight of my body was totally carried by the *Piuma*." The test flight lasted for two hours.

The event won the <u>favor</u> of scholars who studied the works of Leonardo. "The idea of his great dream finally coming true really touched me," said one who expressed his approval.

Leonardo dared to think beyond the limits of his age. Unfortunately, his ideas were <u>captive</u>, held prisoners of time. Finally, one of his most daring ideas has been set free.

1. Circle the word that tells what happened to every <u>attempt</u> to fly. Rewrite the sentence, using a synonym for *attempt*.

2. Circle the words that tell what birds gave people a <u>glimpse</u> of. Write the meaning of *glimpse*.

3. Circle the word that is a synonym for <u>liberty</u>. Use the word *liberty* in a sentence.

4. Circle the word that is a synonym for <u>thirst</u>. Use the synonym to write about something you *thirst* for.

5. Underline the words that tell how long of a <u>delay</u> before Leonardo's theory took flight. What does *delay* mean?

6. Underline the names of the materials from which the model was <u>fashioned</u>. Give a synonym for *fashioned*.

7. Circle the word that is a synonym of <u>favor</u>. Use the word *favor* in a sentence.

8. Circle the phrase that means the opposite of <u>captive</u>. Give an example of when a person might be *captive*.

Name _____   Date _____

Read the following passage. Pay special attention to the underlined words. Then, read it again, and complete the activities. Use a separate sheet of paper for your written answers.

Once the plane had soared <u>aloft</u>, up, up, and up, and leveled out, Beckman released his grip on the arms of his seat. Oh, how he hated flying. Feeling <u>imprisoned</u> in a cramped cabin while traveling thousands of feet above the earth was *not* his idea of a good time. Each time he needed to travel cross-country, his choice of transportation <u>wavered</u> between flying and taking the train. To save time, he always ended up flying and he loathed every minute of it.

"Is this your first flight?" the flight attendant asked sweetly.

"Oh no, I fly all the time," Beckman replied, looking decidedly green around the eyes. "Could you bring me some sparkling water? I need to <u>quench</u> my thirst."

"Certainly!" The attendant knew he meant "to settle my stomach," but she just smiled and trotted off.

It was embarrassing. A grown man, an <u>architect</u> who designed billion-dollar buildings, afraid of flying. He knew his fears were groundless—no pun intended! People flew every day. The pilots know their stuff. He would be okay.

He had watched the safety announcement before take-off. A man smiled from the TV screen and reviewed the emergency procedures. "In the event of wind turbulence, please remain seated with your seat belt buckled. Locate the emergency exit nearest to your seat, . . ."

Beckman took the man's <u>cautions</u> to heart. He checked his seat belt: buckled. He checked the emergency exit: three rows back. The flight attendant arrived with his sparkling water. Beckman opened a magazine, settled back, and tried to read. As he looked out the window, he wondered how the air <u>sustained</u> the weight of the plane. Soon, sleep <u>overtook</u> him. He was still sleeping when the plane landed.

"Well," he thought when he awoke, "that wasn't so bad, after all!"

1. Circle the words that hint at the meaning of <u>aloft</u>. Give an example of something other than a plane that goes *aloft*.

2. Underline the words that tell where Beckman felt <u>imprisoned</u>. Write about a place where you have felt *imprisoned*.

3. Underline the words that describe how Beckman's choices <u>wavered</u>. Write a phrase that means the same thing as *wavered*.

4. Circle the words that tell what Beckman requested to <u>quench</u> his thirst. Write the meaning of *quench*.

5. Underline the words that tell what Beckman did as an <u>architect</u>. Write a sentence using the word *architect*.

6. Underline the words that tell how Beckman took the man's <u>cautions</u> to heart. Write about some *cautions* you take seriously.

7. Circle the word that tells what <u>sustained</u> the weight of the plane. Give a synonym for *sustained*.

8. Circle the word that tells what <u>overtook</u> Beckman. Write the meaning for *overtook*.

Name _____ Date _____

"**Icarus and Daedalus**" by Josephine Preston Peabody

Reading: Ask Questions to Analyze Cause-and-Effect Relationships

A **cause** is an event, action, or feeling that produces a result. An **effect** is the result. In some literary works, multiple causes result in one single effect. In other works, a single cause results in multiple effects. Effects can also become causes for events that follow. The linking of causes and effects propels the action forward.

As you read, **ask questions** such as "What happened?" and "What will happen as a result of this?" **to analyze cause-and-effect relationships.**

DIRECTIONS: *Use the following graphic organizer to analyze some of the cause-and-effect relationships in "Icarus and Daedalus." The first response has been filled in as an example. Where there is no box in which to write the question you would ask yourself, ask the question mentally, and then write the effect in the next box.*

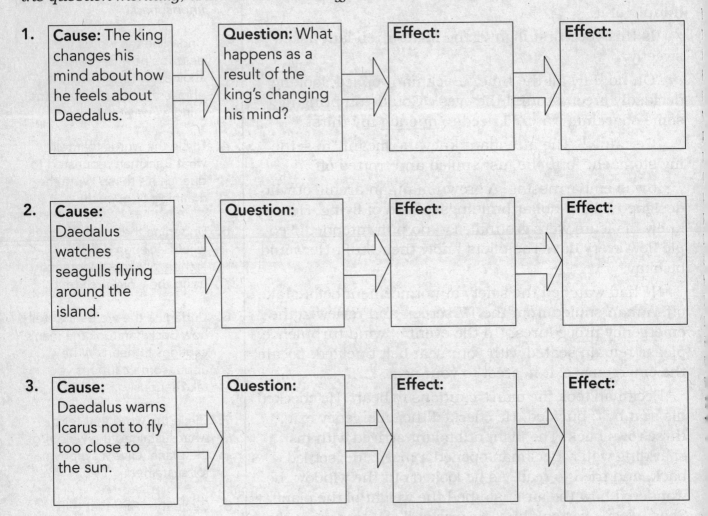

1. **Cause:** The king changes his mind about how he feels about Daedalus. → **Question:** What happens as a result of the king's changing his mind? → **Effect:** → **Effect:**

2. **Cause:** Daedalus watches seagulls flying around the island. → **Question:** → **Effect:** → **Effect:**

3. **Cause:** Daedalus warns Icarus not to fly too close to the sun. → **Question:** → **Effect:** → **Effect:**

Name _____ Date _____

"Icarus and Daedalus" by Josephine Preston Peabody
Literary Analysis: Myth

Since time began, people have tried to understand the world around them. Ancient peoples created **myths**—stories that explain natural occurrences and express beliefs about right and wrong. Every culture has its own collection of myths, or *mythology*. In many myths, gods and goddesses have human traits, and human heroes have superhuman traits. Myths explore universal themes and explain the world in human terms.

Most myths perform some of the following functions:

- explain natural occurrences
- express beliefs about right and wrong
- show gods or goddesses with human traits
- show human heroes with superhuman traits
- explore universal themes

Not all myths perform all of those functions, however. "Icarus and Daedalus" illustrates only a few of them.

DIRECTIONS: *Read each excerpt from "Icarus and Daedalus" that follows, and answer the question about the functions of a myth that the excerpt illustrates.*

Among all those mortals who grew so wise that they learned the secrets of the gods, none was more cunning than Daedalus.

1. Which function of a myth does the excerpt illustrate? How can you tell?

_____

_____

_____

"Remember," said the father, "never to fly very low or very high."

2. Which function of a myth does the excerpt illustrate? How can you tell?

_____

_____

_____

The nearest island he named Icaria, in memory of the child; but he, in heavy grief, went to the temple of Apollo in Sicily, and there hung up his wings as an offering. Never again did he attempt to fly.

3. Which function of a myth does the excerpt illustrate? How can you tell?

_____

_____

_____

Name _____   Date _____

"Icarus and Daedalus" by Josephine Preston Peabody
Vocabulary Builder

Word List

<pre>
┌─────────────────────────────────────┐
│   vacancy   sustained   │
└─────────────────────────────────────┘
</pre>

A. DIRECTIONS: *Read each item, and think about the meaning of the underlined word from the Word List. Then, answer the question, and explain your answer.*

1. There is no <u>vacancy</u> at a motel. Can someone get a room there?

_____

_____

2. The villagers felt themselves <u>sustained</u> by the politicians' promises. Did the villagers trust that the promises would be fulfilled?

_____

_____

B. DIRECTIONS: *Revise each sentence so that the underlined vocabulary word is used logically.*

1. The <u>vacancy</u> in the look on the man's face made me think that he had a lot on his mind.

_____

_____

2. <u>Sustained</u> by the food, the villagers were starving.

_____

C. DIRECTIONS: *Write the letter of the word that means the same or about the same as the word from the Word List.*

____ 1. vacancy
    A. property
    B. appointment
    C. emptiness
    D. discount

____ 2. sustained
    A. supported
    B. starved
    C. deprived
    D. competed

Name _____ Date _____

Support for Writing a Myth

Use the following graphic organizer to take notes for a **myth** you will write to explain a natural phenomenon. You do not have to respond to each prompt in the chart in the order in which it appears, but you should probably decide on the phenomenon you want to explain before you decide on anything else. You might describe the problem and the resolution next and then work on the characters. Coming up with the title may be the last thing you do.

Natural phenomenon that myth will explain:
Title of myth:
Names and traits of characters—how they look, what they do, what they say to one another:
Problem to be solved and creative way in which it will be solved:

Now, write the first draft of your myth.

25

Name _____ Date _____

"Icarus and Daedalus" by Josephine Preston Peabody
Support for Extend Your Learning

Research and Technology

As you conduct research for a **poster** or **three-dimensional model** explaining how birds fly, use this chart to make notes on your findings.

Anatomy of a bird, structure of bones and feathers:
Principles of flight:
Materials needed for poster or model:
Steps required to make poster or model:

Listening and Speaking

Before you present your **debate,** discuss the following points with the members of your group. Then, respond to the prompts that follow.

- Daedalus shares some responsibility for what happened to Icarus.
- Icarus alone is responsible for his failure.

My group's argument: _____

Points in support of our argument: _____

_____

_____

Expected arguments by opposition: _____

_____

_____

Our counterarguments: _____

_____

_____

Name _____ Date _____

"Icarus and Daedalus" by Josephine Preston Peabody
Enrichment: Greek Gods and Modern English

The names of many of the Greek gods have entered the English language. For example, Gaea was the goddess of the earth, and we use her name in *geography*, *geology*, and *geometry*, words that describe basic ways of investigating and mapping the earth. All of those words contain the Greek root *-ge-*, meaning "earth." Study this list of names from Greek mythology:

Name	Identification
Chaos	Time of confusion and formlessness, from which Gaea was created
Titans	Group of giant gods
Atlas	Titan who was forced to support the world on his shoulders
Cronus	Titan who was the god of time
Hercules	Half-mortal god known for his immense strength
Pluto	God of the underworld

A. DIRECTIONS: *Use a word from the box to complete each sentence.*

Titanic   chronological   atlas   plutonium   Herculean   chaotic

1. A book of maps is called a(n) _____.

2. Someone who is very strong is said to have _____ strength.

3. The _____, a ship launched in 1912, was the largest vessel of its time.

4. Events placed in the order in which they happened are in _____ order.

5. A confused, disorganized situation may be described as _____.

6. The element named for the planet farthest from the sun is _____.

B. DIRECTIONS: *Use the six words from the box in sentences of your own. Try to use* Titanic *and* atlas *in one sentence,* chronological *and* chaotic *in a second sentence, and* plutonium *and* Herculean *in a third. Consult a dictionary if you are unsure of a word's meaning.*

_____

_____

_____

_____

_____

_____

Name _____ Date _____

"Icarus and Daedalus" by Josephine Preston Peabody
Selection Test A

Critical Reading *Identify the letter of the choice that best answers the question.*

_____ 1. In "Icarus and Daedalus," what event has caused Daedalus to be locked in the tower?
A. He is being punished for trapping the king in his Labyrinth.
B. The king changed his attitude and no longer favors him.
C. He is being punished for playing tricks on the royal court.
D. The king grew angry with him for not working fast enough.

_____ 2. Daedalus is described in "Icarus and Daedalus" as cunning (resourceful). Given that information, what can the reader predict he will do after being imprisoned on the island?
A. plan a way to escape
B. grow to like the island
C. seek advice from his son
D. write a poem criticizing the king

_____ 3. In "Icarus and Daedalus," why does Daedalus associate sea-gulls with liberty?
A. A sea-gull guards him in his prison cell.
B. Sea-gulls can fly freely to and from the island.
C. He thinks that all sea creatures are free.
D. Sea-gulls carry messages from him to Icarus.

_____ 4. In "Icarus and Daedalus," what is the relationship between the two main characters?
A. They are cousins.
B. They are king and subject.
C. They are friends.
D. They are father and son.

_____ 5. According to Daedalus in "Icarus and Daedalus," what will be the effect if Icarus flies too low?
A. The sun's heat will melt his wings.
B. The earth's fog will weigh him down.
C. The tower guards will capture him.
D. His wings will hit the tops of buildings.

Name _____ Date _____

_____ 6. In "Icarus and Daedalus," what is the reason Icarus flies toward "the highest heavens"?
A. He is cold and wants to feel warmer.
B. He does not believe Daedalus's warnings.
C. He trusts that Daedalus's invention will not fail him.
D. He wants to escape the feeling of being held in captivity.

_____ 7. According to "Icarus and Daedalus," why does Icarus fall into the sea?
A. The wings are not big enough to support his weight.
B. The wings melt when he flies too close to the sun.
C. He loses his way when he flies too far from Daedalus.
D. He is blinded when he flies too close to the sun.

_____ 8. In "Icarus and Daedalus," which event shows that in myths, human beings may have superhuman traits?
A. Daedalus builds a labyrinth.
B. King Minos imprisons Daedalus.
C. Daedalus and Icarus are able to fly.
D. Daedalus grieves over his son's death.

_____ 9. What is one lesson taught by "Icarus and Daedalus"?
A. Tyrants like King Minos are always punished.
B. The gods help those who help themselves.
C. Children should never be allowed too much freedom.
D. One should not do more than one is capable of doing.

_____ 10. In terms of a modern-day device, what are the wings that Daedalus invents in "Icarus and Daedalus" most like?
A. an airplane
B. a hydroplane
C. a hang glider
D. a helicopter

Vocabulary and Grammar

_____ 11. Where is there most likely to be a *vacancy*?
A. in a crowded city
B. in a wide-open area
C. in a popular restaurant
D. in a dense forest

Name _____ Date _____

_____ 12. Which phrase most logically completes this sentence?

Sustained by _____, the long-distance runner won the race.

A. intense headaches

B. a desire to fail

C. strong muscles

D. a weak heart

_____ 13. In which sentence is the colon used correctly?

A. Daedalus gathered: feathers, wax, and thread to make wings.

B. The king imprisoned Daedalus in the tower because: his favor shifted.

C. Once he began to fly, Icarus longed for: warmth, freedom, and joy.

D. Daedalus felt these emotions: grief, sadness, and loneliness.

_____ 14. In which sentence is the colon used correctly?

A. Daedalus was skilled at the following: inventing, building, and escaping.

B. When Daedalus was imprisoned, the first thing he did was: escape from his cell.

C. Daedalus invented wings by: watching birds and seeing how they flew.

D. What happened to Icarus was: he fell into the sea and drowned.

Essay

15. "Icarus and Daedalus" contains two main characters: Daedalus and Icarus. Which character do you find more interesting? Why do you find him more interesting? Is it because you are better able to relate to him? Is it because he gives you more to think about? In an essay, tell whether you prefer Icarus or Daedalus, and explain why. Cite two details from the selection to support your opinion.

16. Before they set out on their flight, Daedalus warns Icarus of the dangers, yet Icarus forgets Daedalus's warnings when he tastes the joy of freedom. Do you believe that Daedalus shares in the responsibility for Icarus's death? Did he do everything possible to ensure the safety of Icarus's flight? In an essay, answer those questions. Explain your opinion, and suggest what—if anything—Daedalus might have done differently.

Name _____ Date _____

"Icarus and Daedalus" by Josephine Preston Peabody
Selection Test B

Critical Reading *Identify the letter of the choice that best completes the statement or answers the question.*

____ 1. When "Icarus and Daedalus" opens, Daedalus is watching the flight of sea-gulls. Where is he at that point?
A. He is lost in the Labyrinth that he built.
B. He is imprisoned in a cell in a tower.
C. He is on the island of Crete.
D. He is in a workroom making a pair of wings.

____ 2. Since Daedalus is described in "Icarus and Daedalus" as "cunning" (resourceful), what can the reader predict he will do?
A. admit to the king that he deserves his punishment
B. find a way to escape from the island of Crete
C. bribe the guards to let him out of his prison cell
D. imprison the king in the wonderful Labyrinth

____ 3. In "Icarus and Daedalus," what inspires Daedalus to build the device that will allow him to leave Crete?
A. the Labyrinth he built for King Minos
B. the tower in which he was imprisoned
C. the wax from the candles in his cell
D. the sea-gulls he sees in the sky

____ 4. In "Icarus and Daedalus," to what does Daedalus compare the experience of flying?
A. dying
B. gliding
C. soaring
D. swimming

____ 5. In "Icarus and Daedalus," about what two things does Daedalus warn Icarus when they are about to take flight?
A. the labyrinth and the king
B. the fog and the sun's heat
C. the island and the prison guards
D. the tower and the wind currents

____ 6. Which of these sentences from "Icarus and Daedalus" helps you predict that Icarus will not listen to Daedalus's warnings?
    I. For Icarus, these cautions went in at one ear and out by the other.
    II. Who could remember to be careful when he was to fly for the first time?
    III. And not an idea remained in the boy's head but the one joy of escape.
    IV. At first there was a terror in the joy. The wide vacancy of the air dazed them.
A. I, II, IV
B. II, III, IV
C. I, III, IV
D. I, II, III

___ 7. Why do Daedalus and Icarus not fly hand in hand?
    A. Daedalus is heavier than Icarus.
    B. Their wings would get in each other's way.
    C. Daedalus must fly ahead to plot the route.
    D. Icarus is impatient and wants to be on his own.

___ 8. What do people think when they see Daedalus and Icarus in the sky?
    A. They are birds.
    B. They are gods.
    C. They are prisoners.
    D. They are airplanes.

___ 9. As Icarus flies closer to the sun, what is the cause of the disaster that befalls him?
    A. The light of the sun blinds him.
    B. The heat of the sun burns him.
    C. The height of his flight exhausts him.
    D. The heat of the sun melts his wings.

___ 10. What is another way to express the message in this passage from "Icarus and Daedalus"?
    Remember . . . never to fly very low or very high.

    A. Never fly too far from me.
    B. Never let anyone imprison you.
    C. Never disobey the king.
    D. Never go to extremes.

___ 11. How does Daedalus memorialize Icarus, according to "Icarus and Daedalus"?
    A. He hangs up his wings forever.
    B. He defies Apollo's wishes.
    C. He names a nearby island Icaria.
    D. He dedicates himself to Minos.

___ 12. What element in "Icarus and Daedalus" suggests that the story is a myth?
    A. Daedalus builds a confusing Labyrinth.
    B. Daedalus falls out of favor with the king.
    C. Daedalus possesses superhuman traits.
    D. Daedalus grieves for Icarus's death.

___ 13. Why might a parent tell the story of "Icarus and Daedalus" to a child?
    A. It shows Daedalus as a strong father figure.
    B. It shows that fathers and sons should stick together.
    C. It shows that disobedient children get what they deserve.
    D. It shows that children should obey their parents.

___ 14. What universal theme is implied in "Icarus and Daedalus"?
    A. Mortals should not try to be like the gods.
    B. Fathers should forbid their sons to do dangerous things.
    C. Kings should not imprison innocent people.
    D. Children should never try to do dangerous things.

Vocabulary and Grammar

____ 15. In which sentence is the meaning of the word *vacancy* best expressed?
   A. Escape by sea seemed impossible, for every ship was well guarded.
   B. Over time, Daedalus collected a great many large and small feathers.
   C. The wide emptiness of the air dazed them and made their brains reel.
   D. The heat from the sun had melted the wax on Icarus's wings.

____ 16. Which sentence shows the meaning of the word *sustained*?
   A. At last came a day on which there was a strong wind.
   B. Daedalus and Icarus felt terror as well as joy.
   C. They were thrilled to leave the hateful island of Crete behind.
   D. Icarus felt himself supported by a great wind that filled his wings.

____ 17. In which sentence is the colon used correctly?
   A. The names of some of the Greek gods are: Zeus, Hera, and Apollo.
   B. Myths do the following: explain occurrences, express beliefs, explore themes.
   C. To make his wings, Daedalus gathers feathers: wax: and thread.
   D. Icarus longs for: warmth, freedom, and joy.

____ 18. In which sentence is the colon used correctly?
   A. Daedalus escaped from his cell: and he hoped to escape from Crete.
   B. The ships that sailed to and from the island: they were guarded.
   C. Daedalus felt these emotions: grief, sadness, and loneliness.
   D. People looked up and thought they saw: Apollo and Cupid.

Essay

19. In ancient Greece, a well-known proverb warned, "Nothing to excess." In other words, use moderation—do neither too much nor too little. In an essay, explain how this philosophy is reflected in "Icarus and Daedalus." Consider how moderation would have helped Icarus escape the island. Support your answer with two references to the selection.

20. Do you think that Daedalus and Icarus should have remained prisoners on Crete instead of attempting a dangerous escape? If you believe they should have attempted an escape, do you believe that Daedalus's warnings to Icarus were sufficient? In other words, does Daedalus share in the responsibility for Icarus's death? Did Daedalus do everything possible to ensure the safety of Icarus's flight? In an essay, answer those questions. Explain your opinion, and suggest what—if anything—Daedalus might have done differently.

21. In "Icarus and Daedalus," we learn that Daedalus is a cunning mortal who has learned the secrets of the gods. *Cunning* has both negative and positive meanings. In the negative sense, a cunning person uses cleverness for dishonest purposes. In the positive sense, a cunning person is skillful and resourceful. In an essay, tell what you think Daedalus is like. Is there any dishonesty in him? Is he wrong to attempt something that no human has done before? Is he instead simply a skilled inventor? What else do you learn about him. Cite at least two details from the selection to support your opinion of Daedalus.

Vocabulary Warm-up Word Lists

Study these words from "Demeter and Persephone." Then, complete the activities that follow.

Word List A

descend [dee SEND] *v.* to climb down
  John had to <u>descend</u> into the basement to fix the water heater.

fertile [FER tuhl] *adj.* good for growing crops; fruitful
  Ann spread manure on the soil to make it <u>fertile</u>.

goddess [GAHD is] *n.* female supernatural being
  Early Romans worshiped Venus, the <u>goddess</u> of love.

grim [GRIM] *adj.* gloomy, stern, and unpleasant
  The old house looked <u>grim</u> and uninviting.

harvest [HAHR vist] *n.* the gathering in of crops
  Lisa helped her family bring in the apple <u>harvest</u>.

innocent [IN uh suhnt] *adj.* not guilty of a crime
  They released the prisoner because he was proved <u>innocent</u>.

joyful [JOY fuhl] *adj.* very happy
  The couple's 50th anniversary was a <u>joyful</u> occasion.

toiled [TOYLD] *v.* worked hard at something
  The bricklayer <u>toiled</u> all week to build the fireplace.

Word List B

chariot [CHAR ee uht] *n.* ancient horse-drawn vehicle
  The gladiator rode his <u>chariot</u> into the Coliseum.

defies [dee FYZ] *v.* challenges authority
  A person who <u>defies</u> the rules frequently lands in trouble.

fragrance [FRAY gruhns] *n.* a pleasant smell
  The expensive perfume had a flowery <u>fragrance</u>.

mightily [MYT i lee] *adv.* to do something with great force
  The four-wheel drive pushed <u>mightily</u> up the trail.

pangs [PANGZ] *n.* sudden strong, unpleasant feelings
  The letter from his mom gave Tony <u>pangs</u> of homesickness.

realm [RELM] *n.* a kingdom
  In the fairy tale, Cinderella lives in the <u>realm</u> of Prince Charming.

thistles [THIS uhlz] *n.* a wild, prickly plant
  The <u>thistles</u> growing in the field stuck to our clothes.

veins [VAYNZ] *n.* tubes through which blood flows in the body
  Blood flows easily through clear <u>veins</u>.

Name _____ Date _____

Exercise A *Fill in each blank in the paragraph below with an appropriate word from Word List A. Use each word only once.*

The [1] _____ soil had produced several healthy crops this year.
The farmhands had [2] _____ long and hard to bring in the
[3] _____ before the weather changed. Now the crops were in and the
festival had begun. This was always a [4] _____ celebration. The guests
laughed and joked as they began to [5] _____ the steps into the dining
hall. There, stood a statue of Demeter, the Greek [6] _____ of the
Harvest. Demeter's daughter, Persephone, looking young and [7] _____,
stood beside her. A cheerful fire roared in the fireplace and the table was set for the
feast. The mood was cheery, far from the [8] _____ days of winter that
lay ahead.

Exercise B *Answer the questions with complete explanations.*

Example: If Jane has healthy <u>veins</u>, will her blood flow normally?
Yes, her blood should flow normally through healthy <u>veins</u>.

1. Should parents reward a child who <u>defies</u> them?
   _____

2. If you suffer <u>pangs</u> of regret, would you call a doctor?
   _____

3. To walk through a field of <u>thistles</u>, would you wear boots or sandals?
   _____

4. If a man owns a <u>chariot</u>, does he need hay?
   _____

5. If you wear a heavy <u>fragrance</u>, will it keep you warm?
   _____

6. When a train moves forward <u>mightily</u>, is it easy to jump on board?
   _____

7. If you go into another <u>realm</u>, is it likely you are at home?
   _____

Name _____ Date _____

"Demeter and Persephone" by Anne Terry White
Reading Warm-up A

Read the following passage. Pay special attention to the underlined words. Then, read it again, and complete the activities. Use a separate sheet of paper for your written answers.

Of all the Greek gods and goddesses who ruled over humankind, Hades was the least liked. He was not a cheerful fellow. In fact, he was downright grim compared with his brothers, Zeus and Poseidon. Hades lived in darkness. His favorite color was black. He possessed the riches in the earth but not the fertile, life-giving soil. Nor did the autumn harvest belong to him. His treasures were gems and metals, the non-living things of the earth. Hades ruled the barren Underworld: the Land of the Dead.

According to the early Greeks, when people died, they would descend into the land of Hades. A ferryman, called Charon, rowed them across the River Styx. On the other side of this river, they met the three-headed dog Cerberus. Cerberus guarded the gates into the Underworld and allowed only the dead to pass through. Any living person who wanted to visit a departed loved-one was out of luck!

The early Greeks believed everyone went to the land of Hades after they died—the innocent as well as the guilty. Soldiers who protected the land and farmers who toiled in the fields all went to Hades. If they had lived a good life, however, their time in the Underworld could be pleasant.

Later, Romans adopted the Greek gods and changed their names. *Zeus* became *Jupiter. Poseidon* became *Neptune. Hades* became *Pluto.*

Today people no longer believe in the Greek and Roman gods. Many do not even know who Hades/Pluto was. Nevertheless, he is still with us but in name only. *Pluto* is the name of the ninth and darkest planet in our solar system. The rare metal plutonium is also named after Pluto—and so is the joyful, happy-go-lucky companion of Mickey Mouse, Pluto the dog. What a switch!

1. Underline words that tell what gods and goddesses did. Name some *goddesses* you know about.

2. Circle the word that means the opposite of grim. Rewrite the sentence using a synonym for *grim*.

3. Circle the word that means the opposite of fertile. Write the meaning of *fertile* soil.

4. Underline the words that tell what the harvest did. Use the word *harvest* in a sentence.

5. Underline the words that tell where people would descend. Write a sentence using the word *descend*.

6. Circle the word that means the opposite of innocent. Write the meaning of *innocent*.

7. Underline the words that tell where farmers toiled. Write about something over which you have *toiled*.

8. Circle the words that describe joyful. Describe something you think of as *joyful*.

Name _____ Date _____

"**Demeter and Persephone**" by Anne Terry White
Reading Warm-up B

Read the following passage. Pay special attention to the underlined words. Then, read it again, and complete the activities. Use a separate sheet of paper for your written answers.

"Curtain in five minutes everyone!" called the stage manager. "Five minutes!"

Turner fussed with his costume while trying to remember his opening lines, "Who dares to enter the <u>realm</u> of Pluto? Speak, whoever dares to trespass into my kingdom!"

Someone behind him giggled. "Hey, Pluto, your toga is on backwards."

Turner spun around and saw that Julia was teasing him. Julia was playing the part of his unhappy bride, Persephone. Her crown of dry <u>thistles</u> sat askew on her head. He straightened it carefully so as not to catch his sleeve on the prickly plant. "You should talk," he said roughly.

Julia caught Turner's mood and realized he was suffering <u>pangs</u> of stage fright. "You're going to be great," she said encouragingly.

Turner was not convinced. Rehearsals had been tough, and the role of Pluto was bigger than life. Although he had struggled <u>mightily</u> to learn his part, he couldn't seem to get it right.

"Think!" the director had roared until the <u>veins</u> in his neck seemed about to pop. "You are a god, the mighty Pluto! How do you act when a mortal <u>defies</u> your laws, when a mere *mortal* tries to disobey your command?"

While watching the director, Turner finally understood what he had to do. He began imitating the director's behavior and immediately "got" the character. Unfortunately, he still had trouble standing upright in Pluto's <u>chariot</u>, because the two-wheeled vehicle wobbled back and forth.

"One minute to curtain!" said the stage manager in a loud stage whisper.

As Turner moved toward the curtain he asked over his shoulder, "What's that <u>fragrance</u> you're wearing, Julia? It makes me feel . . . I don't know . . . happy."

"That, my friend, is the sweet smell of success," Julia answered. "Now get out there and let's have some fun!"

1. Circle the word that is a synonym for <u>realm</u>. Write a sentence using the word *realm*.

2. Underline the words that describe <u>thistles</u>. Write a sentence telling where you might find *thistles*.

3. Underline the phrase that describes Turner's <u>pangs</u>. Rewrite the phrase using a synonym for *pangs*.

4. Circle the word that tells what Turner did <u>mightily</u>. Write a sentence using an antonym for *mightily*.

5. Circle the words that tell which of the director's <u>veins</u> seemed to pop. Write the meaning of *veins*.

6. Circle the word that means the same as <u>defies</u>. Write a sentence using the word *defies*.

7. Circle the words that describe a <u>chariot</u>. Tell about another time and place where you might find a *chariot*.

8. Circle the word that is a synonym for <u>fragrance</u>. Write a sentence describing your favorite *fragrance*.

Unit 6 Resources: Themes in the Oral Tradition

Name _____ Date _____

Reading: Ask Questions to Analyze Cause-and-Effect Relationships

A **cause** is an event, action, or feeling that produces a result. An **effect** is the result. In some literary works, multiple causes result in one single effect. In other works, a single cause results in multiple effects. Effects can also become causes for events that follow. The linking of causes and effects propels the action forward.

As you read, **ask questions** such as "What happened?" and "What will happen as a result of this?" **to analyze cause-and-effect relationships.**

DIRECTIONS: *Use the following graphic organizer to analyze some of the cause-and-effect relationships in "Demeter and Persephone." The first response has been filled in as example. Where there is no box in which to write the question you would ask yourself, ask the question mentally, and then write the effect in the next box.*

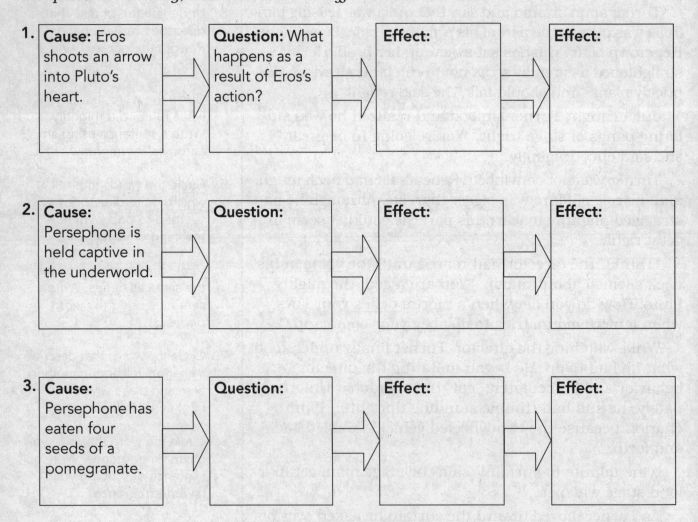

1. **Cause:** Eros shoots an arrow into Pluto's heart. → **Question:** What happens as a result of Eros's action? → **Effect:** → **Effect:**

2. **Cause:** Persephone is held captive in the underworld. → **Question:** → **Effect:** → **Effect:**

3. **Cause:** Persephone has eaten four seeds of a pomegranate. → **Question:** → **Effect:** → **Effect:**

38

"Demeter and Persephone" by Anne Terry White
Literary Analysis: Myth

Since time began, people have tried to understand the world around them. Ancient peoples created **myths**—stories that explain natural occurrences and express beliefs about right and wrong. Every culture has its own collection of myths, or *mythology*. In many myths, gods and goddesses have human traits, and human heroes have superhuman traits. Myths explore universal themes and explain the world in human terms.

Most myths perform some of the following functions:

- explain natural occurrences
- express beliefs about right and wrong
- show gods or goddesses with human traits
- show human heroes with superhuman traits
- explore universal themes

Not all myths perform all of those functions, however. "Demeter and Persephone" illustrates only a few of them.

DIRECTIONS: *Read each excerpt from "Demeter and Persephone" that follows, and answer the question about the function of a myth that the excerpt illustrates.*

Deep under Mt. Aetna, the gods had buried alive a number of fearful, fire-breathing giants. The monsters heaved and struggled to get free. And so mightily did they shake the earth . . .

1. Which function of a myth does the excerpt illustrate? How can you tell?

_____

_____

_____

Now an unaccustomed warmth stole through his veins. His stern eyes softened. . . . The god looked at Persephone and loved her at once.

2. Which function of a myth does the excerpt illustrate? How can you tell?

_____

_____

_____

It seems that all mankind would die of hunger.
"This cannot go on," said mighty Zeus. "I see that I must intervene."

3. Which function of a myth does the excerpt illustrate? How can you tell?

_____

_____

_____

Name _____ Date _____

"Demeter and Persephone" by Anne Terry White
Vocabulary Builder

Word List

defies   intervene

A. DIRECTIONS: *Read each item, and think about the meaning of the underlined word from the Word List. Then, answer the question, and explain your answer.*

1. If a soldier <u>defies</u> orders, is he or she likely to be given a medal?

   _____

   _____

2. If you <u>intervene</u> in a fight, is there a possibility that you will get hurt?

   _____

   _____

B. DIRECTIONS: *Revise each sentence so that the underlined vocabulary word is used logically.*

1. Zeus is pleased when a god or goddess <u>defies</u> his orders.

   _____

2. When the world is calm and at peace, Zeus is likely to <u>intervene</u>.

   _____

C. DIRECTIONS: *Write the letter of the word that means* the same or about the same as *the word from the Word List.*

____ 1. intervene
    A. ignore   C. congregate
    B. interfere   D. lecture

____ 2. defies
    A. competes   C. opposes
    B. compliments   D. reports

Name _____ Date _____

"**Demeter and Persephone**" by Anne Terry White
Support for Writing a Myth

Use the following graphic organizer to take notes for a **myth** you will write to explain a natural phenomenon. You do not have to respond to each prompt in the chart in the order in which it appears, but you should probably decide on the phenomenon you want to explain before you decide on anything else. You might describe the problem and the resolution next and then work on the characters. Coming up with the title may be the last thing you do.

Natural phenomenon that myth will explain:
Title of myth:
Names and traits of characters—how they look, what they do, what they say to one another:
Problem to be solved and creative way in which it will be solved:

Now, write the first draft of your myth.

Name _____ Date _____

"Demeter and Persephone" by Anne Terry White
Support for Extend Your Learning

Research and Technology

As you conduct research for a **poster** or **three-dimensional model** explaining how the position of the Earth and the sun affects the changing of the seasons, use this chart to make notes about your findings.

Position of Earth and sun in relation to the Northern Hemisphere during spring:
Position of Earth and sun in relation to the Northern Hemisphere during summer:
Position of Earth and sun in relation to the Northern Hemisphere during fall:
Position of Earth and sun in relation to the Northern Hemisphere during winter:
Materials needed for poster or model:
Steps required to make poster or model:

Listening and Speaking

Before you present your **debate,** discuss the following points with the members of your group. Then, respond to the prompts that follow.

- Demeter was justified in changing the weather on Earth.
- Demeter was not justified in changing the weather on Earth.

My group's argument: _____

Points in support of our argument: _____

_____

_____

Expected arguments by opposition: _____

_____

_____

Our counterarguments: _____

_____

_____

Name _____ Date _____

"Demeter and Persephone" by Anne Terry White
Enrichment: Gods and Goddesses in Greek Mythology

Much of ancient Greek culture is based on mythology. Although the gods and goddesses look and act much like men and women, they are more heroic, more beautiful, and more powerful than ordinary humans. Here is a list of the most famous Greek gods and goddesses and the realms they ruled over:

God	Domain	Goddess	Domain
Apollo	the sun	Aphrodite	love and beauty
Ares	war	Artemis	the hunt and the moon
Nike	victory	Athena	wisdom
Poseidon	the seas	Demeter	earth and the harvest
Zeus	all the other gods and thunder	Persephone	the underworld and spring

A. DIRECTIONS: *Refer to the list of gods and goddesses to complete these sentences.*

1. _____ lives part-time in the underworld and brings spring to the earth.

2. _____ is responsible for the storms that endanger the lives of sailors.

3. The day is full of light and warmth, thanks to the work of _____.

4. _____ is the goddess who is responsible for education.

5. On the battlefield, _____ and _____ are the gods to count on for support.

6. When _____ is angry, electric storms lash out at the earth.

7. _____ is often pictured wearing braids of corn.

B. DIRECTIONS: *Imagine that you were casting a movie about the gods and goddesses of Greek mythology. Whom might you cast to play the roles of some of the gods and goddesses described on this page? Explain your choices.*

_____

_____

_____

_____

_____

_____

_____

_____

_____

_____

"Icarus and Daedalus" by Josephine Preston Peabody
"Demeter and Persephone" by Anne Terry White
Build Language Skills: Vocabulary

Denotation and Connotation

A word's **denotation** is its literal meaning, the meaning you find when you look up the word in a dictionary. A word's **connotations** are the associations the word has in our culture. For example, the denotation of *consequence* is "something resulting from a cause." In many cases, the connotations of *consequence* are negative. Consider this sentence:

  If you break the law, you will suffer the <u>consequence</u>.

  Clearly, you are not likely to want to have anything to do with that consequence.

  Yet in certain contexts, words have no connotations. For example, *outcome, result,* and *effect* have meanings similar to that of *consequence,* but those words have no negative connotations.

A. DIRECTIONS: *Use a dictionary to look up the meaning of the following words. Write the definition, and indicate whether the connotation is* positive, negative, *or* neutral. *Then, write a sentence using the word in such a way that its connotation is clear.*

1. hero   **Connotation:** _____

   Definition: _____

   Sentence: _____

2. arrogant   **Connotation:** _____

   Definition: _____

   Sentence: _____

Academic Vocabulary Practice

B. DIRECTIONS: *Answer each question using the underlined Academic Vocabulary word. Be sure to include the vocabulary word in your answer.*

1. Why might a player's illness have an <u>effect</u> on his or her soccer game?

   _____

2. Why will a slippery sidewalk <u>affect</u> the speed at which people walk?

   _____

3. What might be a <u>consequence</u> of learning to play the trumpet?

   _____

4. What might <u>occur</u> if someone breaks the law?

   _____

5. Why might you <u>alter</u> your routine?

   _____

"Icarus and Daedalus" by Josephine Preston Peabody
"Demeter and Persephone" by Anne Terry White

Build Language Skills: Grammar

Punctuation: Colons

A **colon** looks like two periods, one above the other (:). Colons are used to introduce a list that follows an independent clause.

> To make wings, Daedalus gathered the following materials: feathers, wax, and thread.

A. PRACTICE: *Each of the following sentences is missing a colon. Rewrite the sentences, and insert a colon in the correct place.*

1. All of the characters in "Demeter and Persephone" are gods or goddesses Aphrodite, Eros, Pluto, Persephone, Demeter, Zeus, and Hermes.

   _____

   _____

2. Daedalus warns Icarus not to do these things fly too low, fly too high, and fly too far from him.

   _____

   _____

B. Writing Application: *Write two sentences about Greek mythology. In each sentence, use a colon to introduce a list.*

_____

_____

_____

_____

_____

_____

_____

_____

_____

_____

_____

_____

_____

"Demeter and Persephone" by Anne Terry White
Selection Test A

Critical Reading *Identify the letter of the choice that best answers the question.*

____ 1. At the beginning of "Demeter and Persephone," what causes the earth to shake?
    A. Pluto riding across the mountains in his golden chariot
    B. fire-breathing monsters struggling to get free
    C. the arrow that Eros shoots at Pluto
    D. the sadness Demeter feels

____ 2. In "Demeter and Persephone," what causes Pluto to fall in love with Persephone?
    A. her exceptional beauty
    B. the arrow Eros shot at him
    C. his desire to settle down
    D. Zeus's command

____ 3. In "Demeter and Persephone," on whom or what does Demeter lay the blame for her daughter's disappearance?
    A. on Pluto
    B. on Eros
    C. on mortals
    D. on the land

____ 4. In "Demeter and Persephone," how does Demeter show her anger at losing her daughter?
    A. She dries up the land.
    B. She vows vengeance on Eros.
    C. She travels to the underworld.
    D. She steals Pluto's horses.

____ 5. What causes Zeus to take action in "Demeter and Persephone"?
    A. He fears that humankind will revolt against the gods.
    B. He fears that humankind will die out from lack of food.
    C. He fears that Demeter will go to war to rescue Persephone.
    D. He fears that he will never again eat fruits and vegetables.

____ 6. According to "Demeter and Persephone," what does Persephone miss most in the underworld?
    A. flowers
    B. rain
    C. food
    D. jewels

_____ 7. In "Demeter and Persephone," why is Persephone sure that Pluto will obey Zeus's command to release her?

A. Pluto and Zeus are brothers.

B. Zeus is the most powerful god.

C. She is unhappy in the underworld.

D. Demeter is more powerful than Pluto.

_____ 8. According to "Demeter and Persephone," why can Persephone not remain on earth all year round?

A. She has eaten four seeds of a pomegranate.

B. She has offended Pluto by not accepting his gifts.

C. She wants to spend some time in the underworld.

D. She and her mother are not getting along.

_____ 9. Which of the following pairs in "Demeter and Persephone" are parent and child?

    I.   Aphrodite and Eros

    II. Pluto and Persephone

    III. Demeter and Persephone

    IV. Zeus and Demeter

A. I and IV

B. II and IV

C. I and III

D. II and III

_____ 10. What natural occurrence is explained by "Demeter and Persephone"?

A. floods

B. famines

C. earthquakes

D. seasons

_____ 11. Which of the following describes a human trait expressed by a god in "Demeter and Persephone"?

A. Demeter's ability to make the land barren

B. Pluto's ability to fall in love with Persephone

C. The gods' ability to bury giants in the earth

D. Hermes' ability to fly with wings on his feet

_____ 12. "Demeter and Persephone" describes the actions of gods. Therefore, what kind of work can you conclude that it is?

A. a tall tale

B. science fiction

C. a myth

D. a ballad

Vocabulary and Grammar

_____ 13. In which sentence is the word *defies* used correctly?

A. A god *defies* Aphrodite by refusing to fall in love.

B. Demeter *defies* Persephone by welcoming her daughter home.

C. Hermes *defies* Zeus by obeying his command.

D. Persephone *defies* Pluto by returning to him for four months.

_____ 14. Which of these sentences expresses the meaning of the word *intervene*?

A. Aphrodites does not want any god to resist her power.

B. Zeus hesitates to influence either side in an argument between two gods.

C. Demeter grieves for her daughter without knowing the details of her fate.

D. Because Zeus is all-powerful, he knows where Persephone is.

_____ 15. In which sentence is a colon used correctly?

A. Persephone struggled mightily: but she could not escape.

B. Zeus sent: the gods and goddesses to plead with Demeter.

C. A myth often has the following characters: gods, goddesses, and mortals.

D. Persephone ate four seeds: so she spends four months with Pluto.

Essay

16. Think about the major characters in "Demeter and Persephone": Pluto, Demeter, and Persephone. Which character do you find most appealing? What do you like about him or her? In an essay, discuss the reasons for your choice. Cite two details from the selection to support your points.

17. By the conclusion of "Demeter and Persephone," three characters—Demeter, Pluto, and Persephone—experience a partial loss. Do you think that the loss suffered by any one of those characters is greater than that suffered by the other two? If not, explain why all three characters suffer equally. If you believe that one character's suffering is greater than that of the other two, explain your ideas. Which character suffers the most? Why? Cite two details from the selection to support your points.

Unit 6 Resources: Themes in the Oral Tradition
48

Name _____ Date _____

"**Demeter and Persephone**" by Anne Terry White
Selection Test B

Critical Reading *Identify the letter of the choice that best completes the statement or answers the question.*

____ 1. In "Demeter and Persephone," which natural occurrence is most likely being referred to by the fire-breathing giants heaving and struggling beneath Mt. Aetna?
A. a tornado
B. an avalanche
C. an earthquake
D. a volcano

____ 2. In "Demeter and Persephone," what is Eros the god of?
A. love
B. spring
C. the underworld
D. the harvest

____ 3. When Pluto first falls in love with Persephone in "Demeter and Persephone," he
A. gives her jewels.
B. gives her flowers.
C. kidnaps her.
D. courts her.

____ 4. In "Demeter and Persephone," who helps Demeter learn what has become of Persephone?
A. a mortal
B. Pluto
C. Eros
D. a nymph

____ 5. What is Demeter's response to the disappearance of her daughter in "Demeter and Persephone"?
A. She travels to the underworld.
B. She punishes the innocent land.
C. She pleads with Zeus.
D. She punishes Eros.

____ 6. In what way are Zeus and Pluto related in "Demeter and Persephone"?
A. They are father and son.
B. They are uncle and nephew.
C. They are brothers.
D. They are cousins.

___ 7. In "Demeter and Persephone," why does Zeus plead with Demeter before confronting Pluto?
   A. Zeus is uncomfortable with Pluto.
   B. Zeus and Demeter are good friends.
   C. Zeus does not want to hurt Pluto.
   D. Zeus has no sympathy for Demeter.

___ 8. In "Demeter and Persephone," why does Zeus intervene to return Persephone to her mother?
   A. He wants Demeter to stop crying.
   B. He wants Pluto to marry someone else.
   C. He wants to save the human race.
   D. He wants to punish Eros.

___ 9. In "Demeter and Persephone," why does Zeus have the power to interfere in Pluto's life?
   A. Zeus is the king of the gods.
   B. Zeus is older than Pluto.
   C. Pluto has asked Zeus's advice.
   D. Demeter has threatened Zeus.

___ 10. What action by Persephone affects her stay on earth in "Demeter and Persephone"?
   A. She has eaten food in the underworld.
   B. She has worn jewels in the underworld.
   C. She has talked about the underworld.
   D. She has defied Pluto's wishes.

___ 11. According to "Demeter and Persephone," what season do we have as a result of Persephone's actions in the underworld?
   A. winter
   B. spring
   C. summer
   D. fall

___ 12. When Persephone returns to earth in "Demeter and Persephone," Pluto is described as having "a heavy heart." What is meant by that description?
   A. He has heart disease.
   B. He is serious.
   C. He is sad.
   D. He is ill.

___ 13. What natural occurrence is explained by Persephone's return to earth?
   A. the change of the seasons
   B. the melting of the snow
   C. the distinction between night and day
   D. the passage of time during the year

___ 14. Based on the events in "Demeter and Persephone," what can you predict Pluto will do while Persephone is away?
  A. roam the earth
  B. cause a war among the mortals
  C. stop loving her
  D. wait for her to return

___ 15. What is one message of "Demeter and Persephone"?
  A. Jewels are no substitute for flowers.
  B. Gods should not fall in love.
  C. Humans cannot affect the seasons.
  D. You cannot force someone to love you.

___ 16. Because "Demeter and Persephone" uses gods and goddesses to explore the love between a mother and her child, what kind of work can you conclude that it is?
  A. a legend
  B. a poem
  C. a myth
  D. a play

Vocabulary and Grammar

___ 17. Which sentence demonstrates the meaning of the word *intervene*?
  A. Hermes eagerly carries out Zeus's orders.
  B. In the underworld, Pluto gives Persephone jewels.
  C. Demeter and Persephone are reunited at the temple.
  D. Zeus tries to persuade Demeter to stop punishing the land.

___ 18. In which sentence is the colon used correctly?
  A. Persephone spends three seasons on earth: spring, summer, and fall.
  B. Hermes drove the black horses: straight to the temple of Demeter.
  C. Zeus knew that Persephone was: with Pluto in the underworld.
  D. When Persephone saw Hermes: her heart leaped for joy.

___ 19. In which sentence is a colon used correctly?
  A. From Pluto, Persephone received: jewels and a pomegranate.
  B. Eros shot an arrow at Pluto: and the god fell in love.
  C. Pluto had seen many beautiful women: but they had left him cold.
  D. Among the things that died were the following: crops, cattle, weeds.

Essay

20. Who do you think is most responsible for the damage done to the earth and human beings in "Demeter and Persephone"—Eros, Pluto, or Demeter? In an essay, explain your choice. Refer to at least two details from the selection to support your explanation.

21. How are the gods in "Demeter and Persephone" like or unlike human beings? In what ways are they similar to human beings, and in what ways are they different? In an essay, respond to these questions. Cite at least three examples from the selection to support your points.

Vocabulary Warm-up Word Lists

Study these words from "Tenochtitlan: Inside the Aztec Capital." Then, complete the activities.

Word List A

adobe [uh DOH bee] *n.* sun-dried brick
   The house was made of <u>adobe</u> covered with plaster.

described [di SKRYBD] *v.* told about in words
   The excited child <u>described</u> her day at the amusement park.

excellent [EK suh luhnt] *adj.* extremely good; superior
   May we compliment the chef on this <u>excellent</u> meal?

fibers [FYE berz] *n.* threads of a fabric
   <u>Fibers</u> from the blanket shed all over the sofa.

gaps [GAPS] *n.* cracks or openings, as in a wall
   The dogs got out through <u>gaps</u> in the fence.

historical [his TAWR i kuhl] *adj.* having happened or existed
   <u>Historical</u> records prove that our families are related.

included [in KLOOD id] *v.* held or contained
   The park <u>included</u> a lovely pond where swans floated lazily.

prevented [pree VENT id] *v.* kept from happening
   Emma's warning <u>prevented</u> us from entering the danger zone.

Word List B

chimneys [CHIM neez] *n.* tall, hollow structures that carry away smoke
   The large house had six <u>chimneys</u> in all.

compounds [KAHM powndz] *n.* walled yards with buildings in them
   People who live in <u>compounds</u> seldom get lonely.

courtyards [KAWRT yahrdz] *n.* open spaces surrounded by walls
   After dinner, the families went to their own <u>courtyards</u> to relax.

enchanted [en CHANT ed] *adj.* under a magic spell
   The characters in the play had been <u>enchanted</u> with magic dust.

grandchildren [GRAND chil dren] *n.* children of one's son or daughter
   Susan sees her <u>grandchildren</u> at least once a week.

households [HOWS hohldz] *n.* people who live in the same home
   When two <u>households</u> merge, they often have too much stuff.

site [SYT] *n.* the place where something is or was located
   The house had been built on the <u>site</u> of an old mill.

utensils [yoo TEN suhlz] *n.* tools
   <u>Utensils</u> we use for meals include forks, knives, and spoons.

Unit 6 Resources: Themes in the Oral Tradition
52

Name _____ Date _____

"Tenochtitlan: Inside the Aztec Capital" by Jacqueline Dineen
Vocabulary Warm-up Exercises

Exercise A *Fill in each blank in the paragraph below with an appropriate word from Word List A. Use each word only once.*

When he got back from his trip, Timothy [1] _____ the many wonderful

things he had seen. He told Sally about the house made of [2] _____,

which was surprisingly cool inside. When he had asked how that was possible, the

guide had told him that all the [3] _____ between the bricks had been

filled in. Also, the house was actually made of two layers of sun-dried bricks. In between

the layers was another layer of straw [4] _____. This filling provided

[5] _____ insulation and [6] _____ cold from getting

in and heat from getting out. Timothy told Sally that the tour guide had

[7] _____ all sorts of information about the area. He was happy to

learn the [8] _____ importance of the place.

Exercise B *Answer the questions with complete explanations.*

1. What might you find on the <u>site</u> of an abandoned campground?
   _____

2. What kinds of <u>utensils</u> would you use to plant some flowers?
   _____

3. What is the usual cure for an <u>enchanted</u> princess in a fairy tale who has fallen into
   a deep sleep?
   _____

4. What would happen if you had fireplaces but no <u>chimneys</u> in a house?
   _____

5. Name one advantage to living in <u>compounds</u> rather than in separate dwellings.
   _____

6. If you joined <u>households</u> with your best friend, how many people would be living
   together?
   _____

7. What is one way <u>grandchildren</u> can show their love for grandparents?
   _____

8. Do you prefer <u>courtyards</u> or back yards? Why?
   _____

"Tenochtitlan: Inside the Aztec Capital" by Jacqueline Dineen

Reading Warm-up A

Read the following passage. Pay special attention to the underlined words. Then, read it again, and complete the activities. Use a separate sheet of paper for your written answers.

<u>Adobe</u> is an ancient, <u>historical</u> building material. It is made by mixing materials such as sand, clay, water, and sometimes gravel. Often, <u>fibers</u> of hay or grass are added to bind the material. Once the material is mixed, it is shaped by hand into bricks. The bricks are put into molds. Then they are dried in the sun.

The biggest problem in building with adobe is the fact that the material itself is unstable. It changes depending on the amount of water in the air. The more water the bricks absorb, the weaker they become. As the water evaporates, the bricks tend to shrink. Such shrinkage can lead to <u>gaps</u> between the bricks. This problem cannot be <u>prevented</u>, but it can be solved.

Mortar can be used between the bricks to minimize the problem of the gaps. Also, the finished structure can be coated with another material. Mud plaster is one option. This is made of the same ingredients as adobe— clay, sand, water, and straw or grass. Pink or ochre pigments can be <u>included</u>, if desired. The mud plaster is then smoothed over the bricks.

Another coating option is whitewash. This material can be <u>described</u> as ground gypsum rock, water, and clay. This is brushed onto the finished adobe wall. The problem with whitewash is that it wears off and needs to be reapplied every year.

Lime plaster, which is harder than mud plaster, is another choice. It is made of lime, sand, and water. Heavy trowels or brushes are used to apply it over the adobe surface.

Since the early 1900s, cement stucco has been used to coat adobe surfaces. Cement stucco is made of cement, sand, and water. It must be applied over a wire mesh attached to the adobe. This is an <u>excellent</u> choice because it needs little maintenance.

1. Underline the words that mean the same as <u>adobe</u>. Use *adobe* in a sentence.

2. Circle the word that hints at the meaning of <u>historical</u>. Name a *historical* event that you wish you could have seen in person.

3. Underline the words that tell what kind of <u>fibers</u> were used with the mixture. What are *fibers*?

4. Circle the words that tell where the <u>gaps</u> might be. What does the word *gaps* mean?

5. Underline the word that tells what problem cannot be <u>prevented</u>. Describe a problem that you once *prevented*.

6. Circle the words that tell what can be <u>included</u> in the mud plaster. Use *included* in a sentence.

7. Underline the word that tells what is being <u>described</u>. How would you like to be *described*?

8. Circle the words that tell why cement stucco is an <u>excellent</u> choice. What is one *excellent* choice you made recently?

"Tenochtitlan: Inside the Aztec Capital" by Jacqueline Dineen
Reading Warm-up B

Read the following passage. Pay special attention to the underlined words. Then, read it again, and complete the activities. Use a separate sheet of paper for your written answers.

Ever since she read about how the ancient Aztecs lived, Alicia had been <u>enchanted</u> with their way of life. It seemed like a simpler, slower time. People probably enjoyed life more, Alicia thought. She was not sure how accurate her ideas were, but she did think that modern life was too hectic.

Alicia liked the idea of individual <u>households</u> that included extended family. She enjoyed the vision of the different generations living in different wings of the home and sharing common space in the middle. Such <u>compounds</u> were not common in Alicia's time, so she could only imagine the benefits they offered.

For one thing, grandparents and their <u>grandchildren</u> could see each other every day. Thinking about her own grandparents and how little she saw them made Alicia long for a different way of life. She thought about how much easier it would be for young parents to have built-in help with their growing families.

In her imagination, Alicia designed a perfect little village. Each house was on a picturesque <u>site</u> overlooking a lake. The village was full of <u>courtyards</u> where families could gather and visit. Because each generation had a separate wing, each house would have several fireplaces and <u>chimneys</u>.

Gardens would be cultivated both for beauty and for practical reasons. They would grow flowers of all shapes, colors, and sizes. They would grow their own vegetables, like corn, tomatoes, lettuce, and onions. They would even grow their own fruit, like pears (Alicia's favorite), apples, and oranges. Even though she knew this was a fantasy, Alicia enjoyed thinking about it. Each night, as she washed the dishes, <u>utensils</u>, and glasses her family had used at dinner, she would daydream. Someday, she hoped, she could make her ideas a reality.

1. Underline the words that tell what <u>enchanted</u> Alicia. Use *enchanted* in a sentence.

2. Circle the word that describes <u>households</u>. What does the word *households* mean?

3. Underline the words that tell what the Aztec <u>compounds</u> were like. Define *compounds*.

4. Circle the words that tell what grandparents and their <u>grandchildren</u> could do. Use *grandchildren* in a sentence.

5. Underline the word that describes <u>site</u>. Describe a *site* for a home you would like to have.

6. Circle the words that tell what families could do in their <u>courtyards</u>. What does *courtyards* mean?

7. Underline the word that names things that require <u>chimneys</u>. Use *chimneys* in a sentence.

8. Circle the words that tell what Alicia washed in addition to the <u>utensils</u>. What are *utensils*?

Name _____ Date _____

Reading: Reread to Look for Connections That Indicate Cause-and-Effect Relationships

A **cause** is an event or situation that produces a result. An **effect** is the result produced. In a story or an essay, each effect may eventually become a cause for the next event. This series of events results in a cause-and-effect chain, which propels the action forward.

As you read, think about the causes and effects of events. If you do not see a clear cause-and-effect relationship in a passage, **reread to look for connections** in the text. Look for words and phrases that identify cause-and-effect relationships, for example, *because, due to, for that reason, therefore,* and *as a result.*

DIRECTIONS: *Read the following sequences of events. Underline any words or phrases that help you identify a cause-and-effect relationship. Then, identify each event as a* cause, *an* effect, *or both* cause and effect.

_____ 1. The Aztecs were excellent engineers.

_____ 2. Therefore, they were able to build three causeways linking the island city to the mainland.

_____ 3. Because of their skill as engineers, they were also able to build bridges that could be removed.

_____ 4. As a result, they could prevent their enemies from reaching the city.

_____ 5. The land around Lake Texcoco was dry.

_____ 6. Because the land was dry, the Aztecs built ditches to irrigate the land.

_____ 7. As they dug, they piled up the earth from the ditches in shallow parts of the lake, thus forming swamp gardens.

_____ 8. Because they had formed swamp gardens, they had land on which to grow crops.

_____ 9. Because they had land on which to grow crops, a portion of the population was able to grow its own food.

_____ 10. Two of the lakes that fed into Lake Texcoco contained salt water.

_____ 11. For that reason, the Aztecs built an embankment to keep out the salt water.

_____ 12. The embankment also protected the city from floods.

"Tenochtitlan: Inside the Aztec Capital" by Jacqueline Dineen
Literary Analysis: Legends and Facts

A **legend** is a traditional story about the past. Legends are based on facts that have grown into fiction over generations of retelling. Legends usually include these elements: a larger-than-life hero or heroine; fantastic events; roots, or a basis, in historical facts; and actions and events that reflect the culture that created the legend.

A **fact** is something that can be proved true. We uncover facts about ancient cultures by studying a variety of sources: written material, paintings, objects, and excavated ruins. When historians are unable to prove a theory about the past, they may speculate, or make a guess, based on the available evidence.

DIRECTIONS: *Read each excerpt from "Tenochtitlan: Inside the Aztec Capital." Then, tell whether the statement describes a* fact *or a* speculation, *and explain how you know.*

1. The Aztecs . . . built three causeways over the swamp to link the city with the mainland.

   Fact / Speculation: _____ **Explanation:** _____

   _____

2. These bridges could be removed to leave gaps and this prevented enemies from getting to the city.

   Fact / Speculation: _____ **Explanation:** _____

   _____

3. The Spaniards' first view of Tenochtitlan was described by one of Cortés's soldiers, Bernal Diaz.

   Fact / Speculation: _____ **Explanation:** _____

   _____

4. Tenochtitlan was built in a huge valley, the Valley of Mexico.

   Fact / Speculation: _____ **Explanation:** _____

   _____

5. Archaeologists think that when Tenochtitlan was at its greatest, about one million people lived in the Valley of Mexico.

   Fact / Speculation: _____ **Explanation:** _____

   _____

6. Historians are not sure how many people in Tenochtitlan were farmers, but they think it may have been between one third and one half of the population.

   Fact / Speculation: _____ **Explanation:** _____

   _____

"Tenochtitlan: Inside the Aztec Capital" by Jacqueline Dineen
Vocabulary Builder

Word List

outskirts	reeds	goblets

A. DIRECTIONS: *Read each item, and think about the meaning of the underlined word from the Word List. Then, answer each question, and explain your answer.*

1. Poorer people lived on the <u>outskirts</u> of Tenochtitlan. Did they live near the Temple Mayor?

   _____

2. <u>Reeds</u> were cut down in the swamps, dried, and woven into baskets. Are reeds trees?

   _____

3. The host passed <u>goblets</u> to his guests. Was he serving food?

   _____

B. DIRECTIONS: *Revise each sentence so that the underlined vocabulary word is used logically. Be sure to use the vocabulary word in your revised sentence.*

1. Michael liked living on the <u>outskirts</u> of the city so that he could be close to the center of activity.

   _____

   _____

2. The builders used <u>reeds</u> for the foundation, to bear the weight of the three-story house.

   _____

   _____

3. The servants placed slabs of juicy meat on the <u>goblets</u>.

   _____

C. DIRECTIONS: *Write the letter of the word that means the same or about the same as the word from the Word List.*

____ 1. outskirts
   A. dresses   B. suburbs   C. contests   D. cities

____ 2. reeds
   A. books   B. swamps   C. castles   D. grasses

____ 3. goblets
   A. cups   B. plates   C. silverware   D. ghosts

Name _____ Date _____

"Tenochtitlan: Inside the Aztec Capital" by Jacqueline Dineen
Support for Writing a Description

Use this chart to take notes as you prepare to write a **description** of Tenochtitlan. Write down as many details as you can to describe the various aspects of the city. Include verbs and adjectives that appeal to the five senses: sight, touch, taste, smell, and hearing.

Tenochtitlan: The Aztec Capital

When did Tenochtitlan exist?	
Where was the city located?	
What was the location of the city like?	
What was the surrounding area like?	
What kinds of infrastructures (roads, bridges, waterways, and so on) did the residents build?	
How did the residents feed themselves?	
What were the homes of the wealthy residents like?	
What were the homes of the poorer residents like?	

Now, use your notes to write a draft of a description of Tenochtitlan. Be sure to use vivid verbs and adjectives that will make your description interesting to your readers. Use words that appeal to the senses of sight, touch, taste, smell, and hearing.

"Tenochtitlan: Inside the Aztec Capital" by Jacqueline Dineen
Support for Extend Your Learning

Research and Technology

As you do research for a **brief report** on how Tenochtitlan developed over time, use this chart. Make notes about what became of the city at various stages and what it is like today. You might also describe how the city was planned and the important structures that were built to help the city function successfully.

Plan of city:	
Engineered structures:	
Changes in city over time:	
What is left of city today:	
What is in place of city today:	

Listening and Speaking

Respond to the following prompts as you prepare a **persuasive speech** aimed at convincing authorities that building a city in the middle of a lake is a good idea.

Explanation of position: _____

_____

Main points in support of position (facts, statistics, and quotations by authorities):

_____

_____

_____

_____

Phrases that will remind me of my points: _____

_____

_____

Once you have organized your material, transfer your notes to cards that you can refer to as you deliver your speech.

Name _____ Date _____

"Tenochtitlan: Inside the Aztec Capital" by Jacqueline Dineen
Enrichment: Aztec Words in English

It is believed that the majority of people living in central Mexico before the arrival of the Spanish spoke a language known as Nahuatl. Soon after the Spanish conquest, in the early 1500s, Nahuatl speakers adapted the letters of the Spanish alphabet so that their language could have a written form. As a result, we have documents from the colonial era written in Nahuatl: city records, poetry, formal addresses, and a collection of observations about pre-Conquest culture.

Nahuatl has survived. Dialects of the language are spoken today by more than one million Mexicans. Not unexpectedly, a number of Nahuatl words have entered the English language:

English Words from Nahuatl

avocado	chocolate	mesquite	pulque	tamale
chili	coyote	ocelot	shack	tomato

DIRECTIONS: *Read the Nahuatl word in each numbered item. (Pronounce* tl *as "tul,"* hu *as "w," and* x *as "sh.") Then, study the definition. On the line, write an English word from the box that corresponds to the Nahuatl word.*

_____ 1. **chilli:** a hot red pepper used for seasoning

_____ 2. **ocelotl:** a spotted wildcat of the southwestern United States, Mexico, and South America

_____ 3. **xacalli:** a wooden hut or thatched cabin

_____ 4. **xocolatl:** a candy or drink made from roasted, ground cacao seeds

_____ 5. **mizquitl:** a common tree or shrub of the southwestern United States and Mexico

_____ 6. **tomatl:** a juicy red or yellow fruit eaten as a vegetable

_____ 7. **ahuacatl:** a pear-shaped fruit that has a dark green or black skin and contains a single large seed

_____ 8. **poliuhqui:** a fermented drink made from the agave plant

_____ 9. **coyotl:** a small wolflike mammal of the dog family that lives in U.S. prairies and woodlands

_____ 10. **tamalli:** a dish that is made of cornmeal and meat, wrapped in corn husks, and roasted

Unit 6 Resources: Themes in the Oral Tradition

© Pearson Education, Inc., publishing as Pearson Prentice Hall. All rights reserved.

61

Name _____ Date _____

"Tenochtitlan: Inside the Aztec Capital" by Jacqueline Dineen
Selection Test A

Critical Reading *Identify the letter of the choice that best answers the question.*

____ 1. "Tenochtitlan: Inside the Aztec Capital" is an essay based on fact. What is a fact?
   A. something that happened long ago
   B. something that can be proved true
   C. something that is an opinion
   D. something that is false

____ 2. According to "Tenochtitlan: Inside the Aztec Capital," what is the meaning of the city's name?
   A. Temple of the Goddess of the Corn Plant
   B. Island in the Middle of a Swampy Lake
   C. Place of the Fruit of the Prickly Pear Cactus
   D. Place of the Fruit of the Maguey Cactus

____ 3. Based on your reading of "Tenochtitlan: Inside the Aztec Capital," what can you conclude was the Aztecs' main reason for building their city on an island in a lake?
   A. to have a regular supply of cactus
   B. to defend themselves from enemies
   C. to build causeways over the swamp
   D. to build a huge temple to the emperor

____ 4. According to "Tenochtitlan: Inside the Aztec Capital," how did the residents of Tenochtitlan get fresh water?
   A. by animal transport
   B. through canals
   C. by slave labor
   D. through aqueducts

____ 5. According to "Tenochtitlan: Inside the Aztec Capital," what was the Spaniards' response when they first saw Tenochtitlan?
   A. astonishment
   B. boredom
   C. puzzlement
   D. ridicule

____ 6. According to "Tenochtitlan: Inside the Aztec Capital," what evidence suggests that corn was precious to Aztec society?

A. Only nobles could eat it.

B. Only priests could raise it.

C. Aztec manuscripts make many references to it.

D. Special gods and goddesses were in charge of it.

____ 7. According to "Tenochtitlan: Inside the Aztec Capital," how did residents of the city travel from place to place?

A. by foot

B. by wagon

C. by canoe

D. by donkey

____ 8. "Tenochtitlan: Inside the Aztec Capital" states or suggests that the Aztecs used water for which of the following purposes?

    I. crop irrigation

    II. drinking

    III. recreation

    IV. canals

A. I, II, III

B. I, III, IV

C. II, III, IV

D. I, II, IV

____ 9. Which of the following sentences about "Tenochtitlan: Inside the Aztec Capital" contains purely factual information?

A. Archaeologists estimate that as many as one million people lived in the Valley of Mexico.

B. Many residents of Tenochtitlan depended on food from outside the city.

C. Historians think that at least one third of Tenochtitlan's residents were farmers.

D. The houses of the city's poor were probably dark, smoky, and unpleasant.

____ 10. According to "Tenochtitlan: Inside the Aztec Capital," which of the following could provide food for one family?

A. a chinampa

B. a maguey cactus

C. a flock of turkeys

D. a farm outside the city

___ 11. According to "Tenochtitlan: Inside the Aztec Capital," why did the Aztecs grow the maguey cactus?

A. It thrives on arid land.

B. It has many uses.

C. It is beautiful.

D. It is fragrant.

___ 12. According to "Tenochtitlan: Inside the Aztec Capital," which of the following is a source of information about Tenochtitlan?

A. the memoirs of Acamapichtli

B. an account by Bernal Diaz

C. an account by Hernando Cortés

D. oral histories by the Aztecs

Vocabulary and Grammar

___ 13. In which sentence is the word *reeds* used correctly?

A. Aztecs used *reeds* to grow crops.

B. Aztecs used *reeds* to make pulque.

C. People slept on mats made of *reeds*.

D. Clothes were made of woven *reeds*.

___ 14. In which sentence is the comma or commas used correctly?

A. The maguey cactus was used for its needles, fiber, and liquid.

B. Farmers had only simple tools, the soil was extremely fertile.

C. The Aztecs constructed aqueducts, and built many causeways.

D. Houses in Tenochtitlan were built of adobe, or of wattle-and-daub.

Essay

15. Writers write articles for a variety of reasons. They may wish to share personal information or persuade readers to their way of thinking. They may wish to inform readers about something or amuse them. For what reason did Jacqueline Dineen write "Tenochtitlan: Inside the Aztec Capital"? In an essay, explain why you think Dineen wrote the article. Cite two details from the article to support your choice.

16. "Tenochtitlan: Inside the Aztec Capital" suggests a number of cause-and-effect relationships. For example, because there was no fresh water in the city, the Aztecs brought water to the city. In that case, the cause is the lack of fresh water. The effect is what the Aztecs did to solve the problem. In an essay, describe a cause-and-effect relationship relating to one of the following facts. In other words, tell what the Aztecs did because of one of these situations:

• Tenochtitlan was built on an island in a swampy lake.

• One swamp garden could provide food for only one family.

Unit 6 Resources: Themes in the Oral Tradition

Name _____ Date _____

"Tenochtitlan: Inside the Aztec Capital" by Jacqueline Dineen
Selection Test B

Critical Reading *Identify the letter of the choice that best completes the statement or answers the question.*

____ 1. "Tenochtitlan: Inside the Aztec Capital" is an essay based on fact. Which definition best describes a fact?
   A. a statement in an encyclopedia
   B. a statement that can be proved true
   C. a statement made long ago
   D. a statement that predicts an event

____ 2. According to "Tenochtitlan: Inside the Aztec Capital," to what was the name "The Place of the Fruit of the Prickly Pear Cactus" first given?
   A. a canal
   B. a chinampa
   C. a city
   D. a temple

____ 3. According to "Tenochtitlan: Inside the Aztec Capital," what is the main reason the Aztecs built causeways?
   A. to bring fresh water to the city
   B. to prevent enemies from entering the city
   C. to connect the city to the mainland
   D. to irrigate the farmland

____ 4. Based on your reading of "Tenochtitlan: Inside the Aztec Capital," what can you conclude was an important reason for the Aztecs' building their capital in the middle of a lake?
   A. to have access to fresh water
   B. to honor the Storm Goddess
   C. to provide a defense against enemies
   D. to practice their skill at engineering

____ 5. According to "Tenochtitlan: Inside the Aztec Capital," what prevented enemies from getting to the city?
   A. warriors stationed along the causeways
   B. removable bridges on the causeways
   C. a moat surrounding the city
   D. an army stationed in the city

____ 6. According to "Tenochtitlan: Inside the Aztec Capital," what was the source of the water in Lake Texcoco?
   A. rivers flowing from mountains
   B. underground springs
   C. irrigation canals
   D. the Gulf of Mexico

_____ 7. Speculation is a conclusion based on guesswork rather than fact. Which of the following sentences about "Tenochtitlan: Inside the Aztec Capital" is a speculation rather than a fact?
A. Archaeologists think that one million people lived in the Valley of Mexico.
B. The Aztecs rebuilt their temples on the same site every 52 years.
C. Fresh water was brought from the mainland to the city by aqueducts.
D. The Aztecs piled up the earth to make swamp gardens, called chinampas.

_____ 8. According to "Tenochtitlan: Inside the Aztec Capital," historians are not sure of the facts about which topic?
A. the location of Tenochtitlan
B. the importance of corn and maguey
C. the use of cacao to make chocolate
D. the number of farmers in Tenochtitlan

_____ 9. Based on your reading "Tenochtitlan: Inside the Aztec Capital," what can you conclude was the reason corn was featured in the Aztec codex?
A. Corn was protected by the gods.
B. Corn was the main Aztec crop.
C. Corn was disliked by the Spanish.
D. Corn was easy to draw and paint.

_____ 10. According to "Tenochtitlan: Inside the Aztec Capital," which members of Aztec society were most like the nobles in social status?
A. the farmers
B. the engineers
C. the priests
D. the craftspeople

_____ 11. According to "Tenochtitlan: Inside the Aztec Capital," the grander houses were whitewashed. Because of the whitewashing, they
A. shone in the sun.
B. were always clean.
C. were protected from bad weather.
D. stood apart from the temples.

_____ 12. Which sentence from "Tenochtitlan: Inside the Aztec Capital" contains a word that signals a cause-and-effect relationship?
A. The twin temple stood on one side, and the king's palace on another.
B. The land around the lakes was dry because there was very little rain.
C. Most people in Tenochtitlan depended on food from outside the city.
D. The courtyards were planted with flower and vegetable gardens.

_____ 13. What is the subject of "Tenochtitlan: Inside the Aztec Capital"?
A. the Aztec people
B. contemporary archaeologists
C. the Spanish explorers
D. contemporary Mexicans

Name _____ Date _____

Vocabulary and Grammar

____ 14. Which sentence expresses the meaning of the word *outskirts*?
   A. Tenochtitlan was built on an island in Lake Texcoco.
   B. Poor people lived in areas far from the heart of the city.
   C. The emperor's palace was made up of several buildings.
   D. Houses had no doors or windows, and they were smoky.

____ 15. Which sentence refers to the use of *goblets*?
   A. Families had containers from which they drank pulque.
   B. Everyone slept on the floor on mats made of reeds.
   C. Households had stones for grinding corn into flour.
   D. Many families had beehives and kept turkeys in pens.

____ 16. Which of the following sentences uses a comma correctly?
   A. The houses were one story high, and they had flat roofs.
   B. Tenochtitlan was by that time, the largest city in Mexico.
   C. One family, could live off the food produced on a chinampa.
   D. There were, few roads, travel was largely by canoe.

____ 17. In which sentence is the semicolon used correctly?
   A. The embankment kept out salt water; and it protected Tenochtitlan from flooding.
   B. Tenochtitlan was built in a huge valley; called the Valley of Mexico.
   C. The city grew larger; more land was drained for farming.
   D. Farmers grew these crops; tomatoes, beans, chili peppers.

Essay

18. "Tenochtitlan: Inside the Aztec Capital" reveals quite a bit about Aztec society—for example, we learn that there was an emperor, or king. Who else made up the society? Were there wealthy people and poor people? What kinds of jobs did people have? In an essay, describe what you learned about Aztec society. Cite at least three details from the article to support your description.

19. The Aztecs had to solve a number of basic problems in order to build a city the size of Tenochtitlan. In an essay, describe how the Aztecs solved the problem of securing an adequate supply of food. Where did the people get the food they ate? What steps did they take to ensure that there was water to irrigate crops? Cite at least two facts from "Tenochtitlan: Inside the Aztec Capital" to support your explanation.

20. Historians discover facts about earlier cultures in a variety of ways. In an essay, describe what one of these illustrations accompanying "Tenochtitlan: Inside the Aztec Capital" tells you about the Aztecs:

   • the map of the city
   • the photograph of maguey cactus plants
   • the drawing of the emperor's palace

   Describe at least two things that the illustration—and the accompanying caption—reveal about Tenochtitlan.

Vocabulary Warm-up Word Lists

Study these words from "Popocatepetl and Ixtlaccihuatl." Then, complete the activities that follow.

Word List A

behalf [bee HAF] *n.* support
 The lawyer acted on <u>behalf</u> of the prisoner.

capacity [kuh PAS i tee] *n.* ability, talent, or skill
 Theresa has a great <u>capacity</u> for kindness.

capital [KAP i tl] *n.* the seat of government
 The <u>capital</u> of Italy is Rome.

coastal [KOHS tuhl] *adj.* of, on, or near the seashore
 Hermosa Beach is a charming <u>coastal</u> city in Southern California.

conflict [KAHN flikt] *n.* a struggle, fight, or battle
 The <u>conflict</u> in the Middle East has been going on for a long time.

emperor [EM per er] *n.* ruler over several kingdoms or countries
 The <u>emperor</u> decreed that all towns would pay more taxes.

peril [PER uhl] *n.* danger
 The shark presented a great <u>peril</u> to the surfers.

siege [SEEJ] *n.* a surrounding of a city by an enemy force
 The <u>siege</u> ended when the town surrendered.

Word List B

approximately [uh PRAHK suh mit lee] *adv.* about; around
 We had <u>approximately</u> two inches of rain last night.

bribe [BRYB] *n.* a gift offered in exchange for a favor
 It is against the law to offer a <u>bribe</u> to a police officer.

exhibited [ig ZIB it ed] *v.* displayed or showed publicly
 Marla <u>exhibited</u> great courage when she made that dangerous play.

fragments [FRAG muhnts] *n.* parts broken off or incomplete
 Dave swept up the <u>fragments</u> of the broken mirror.

outcome [OWT kum] *n.* a result or conclusion
 The <u>outcome</u> of the mystery is still unknown.

pyramid [PEER uh mid] *n.* a structure having four sides shaped like triangles that meet in a point at the top
 We visited a <u>pyramid</u> in Mexico and marveled at its size.

reign [RAYN] *n.* the period during which a king or queen rules
 Shakespeare wrote during the <u>reign</u> of Queen Elizabeth.

variety [vuh RYE i tee] *n.* an absence of sameness; diversity
 The vase contains a <u>variety</u> of summer flowers.

"Popocatepetl and Ixtlaccihuatl" by Julie Piggott Wood
Vocabulary Warm-up Exercises

Exercise A *Fill in each blank in the paragraph below with an appropriate word from Word List A. Use each word only once.*

Nicholas wanted to grow up to be [1] _____ of fourteen countries. His mother told him that was an unusual ambition for a boy who always tried to avoid [2] _____ with others. Nicholas laughed and told her that he was not really afraid to put himself in [3] _____, if it would help him achieve his dream. "On [4] _____ of all underdogs, I declare that I will rule with great compassion," he claimed. "All [5] _____ areas will be open for surfers and swimmers. The [6] _____ of my country will be this very city! Those who object to this will be put under [7] _____ until they change their minds!" His mother reminded herself that Nicholas had a great [8] _____ for wild imagination.

Exercise B *Answer the questions with complete sentences or explanations.*

1. Is a <u>bribe</u> something you would be proud to take? Explain.

   _____

2. If it were your job to <u>reign</u> over a country, what would be your first act?

   _____

3. What are the actions of a dog who <u>exhibited</u> fear?

   _____

4. If you wanted to make a <u>pyramid</u> shape out of paper, what shapes would you have to cut?

   _____

5. <u>Approximately</u> how much time do you need to get ready for school in the morning?

   _____

6. For you, what is an ideal meal that has foods from a <u>variety</u> of food groups?

   _____

7. What is the expected <u>outcome</u> of a series of swim lessons?

   _____

8. What kinds of <u>fragments</u> might you find on the site of a burned-down house?

   _____

Name _____ Date _____

"Popocatepetl and Ixtlaccihuatl" by Julie Piggott Wood
Reading Warm-up A

Read the following passage. Pay special attention to the underlined words. Then, read it again, and complete the activities. Use a separate sheet of paper for your written answers.

The story of how Cortéz conquered Montezuma and the great Aztec civilization begins in 1519. The Spaniards had already set up colonies in the New World. The Spanish governor in Cuba selected Cortéz to explore the coastal areas of Mexico and Central America. Cortéz set sail with 11 ships, 500 men, and a capacity for adventure.

When he got to the island of Cozumel, he met Gerónimo de Aguilar, a Spaniard who had survived the peril of a shipwreck a few years before. He had learned to speak the native language. Cortéz hired him as an interpreter.

They landed near what is now the city of Veracruz. There, messengers sent on behalf of Montezuma met them. Although he didn't call himself an emperor, Montezuma was the ruler of the Aztecs. He had been told of the approach of the Spaniards. He sent gifts of precious feathers and gold necklaces. Cortéz took the messengers as prisoners. He fired cannons, forcing the messengers to watch. The terrified messengers were then sent home.

Montezuma was puzzled. He had thought that Cortéz was the god Quetzalcoatl, whose return had been predicted for that very year. Various signs had convinced him; now he was not so sure.

By the time Cortéz arrived in Tenochtitlan, the Aztec capital, he had gained allies. Neighboring tribes were the enemies of the Aztecs and were glad to help Cortéz. Montezuma welcomed Cortéz, not realizing the Spaniard's intentions. When it became clear that Cortéz wanted nothing less than all the gold in Mexico, it was too late for Montezuma to do anything. By then, large numbers of the population had died from smallpox, brought in by the Spaniards. The siege of Tenochtitlan lasted several months. By the spring of the following year, the conflict was over. The mighty Aztec empire had fallen to the Spaniards.

1. Underline the words that further describe the coastal areas Cortéz was to explore. What *coastal* area would you especially like to visit, and why?

2. Circle the words that further explain the capacity the men had. For what do you have a great *capacity*?

3. Underline the word that tells what peril Aguilar survived. Name one *peril* that you have survived.

4. Circle the word that explains on whose behalf the messengers came. Describe a time you acted on someone else's *behalf*.

5. Underline the word that means about the same as emperor. Define *emperor*.

6. Circle the word that names the Aztec capital. What is the *capital* of your state?

7. Underline the words that tell how long the siege lasted. What does *siege* mean?

8. Circle the words that tell when the conflict ended. Describe a *conflict* you had with someone recently.

"Popocatepetl and Ixtlaccihuatl" by Julie Piggott Wood
Reading Warm-up B

Read the following passage. Pay special attention to the underlined words. Then, read it again, and complete the activities. Use a separate sheet of paper for your written answers.

Donnie was so excited to have a time machine at last. He decided to go back to the time of the ancient Aztecs in Mexico. He had seen pictures of crumbling Aztec pyramids in books. He wanted to see what a <u>pyramid</u> looked like before <u>fragments</u> of it broke off.

He wanted to go back to the <u>reign</u> of the famous Montezuma, so he set the dial for 1518, one year before the arrival of Cortéz. The trip through the centuries took <u>approximately</u> five minutes in real time.

Donnie was not prepared for what he saw when he got there—the city of Tenochtitlan was beautiful! It was hard to believe that ancient people could have built such a large city without electricity or any modern machines.

He was also not prepared for what happened as soon as he was noticed by the locals. They spoke to him in words he could not understand, and they made a <u>variety</u> of hand signals that he could not interpret. When he did not answer to their satisfaction, they <u>exhibited</u> hostile behavior toward him. He was taken prisoner and brought before the great Montezuma.

He finally began to understand that he was being asked to identify himself. He remembered reading that Montezuma believed that the god Quetzalcoatl would return to Tenochtitlan in 1519. Maybe Donnie had put the wrong year into the dial of the time machine. Donnie knew, however, that he did not look at all like Quetzalcoatl. Montezuma was expecting a light-skinned man with a dark beard, one of the many identities the god was said to take. As he was taken away by the guards, Donnie wondered what would be the <u>outcome</u> of his adventure. Was it possible that a guard might accept a <u>bribe</u>?

1. Underline the word that tells what kind of <u>pyramid</u> Donnie wanted to see. Use *pyramid* in a sentence.

2. Circle the words that tell what happened to the <u>fragments</u>. Use *fragments* in a sentence.

3. Underline the word that tells whose <u>reign</u> Donnie wanted to observe. What does *reign* mean?

4. Circle the words that <u>approximately</u> describes. Define *approximately*.

5. Underline the words further explained by the word <u>variety</u>. Describe a *variety* of hand signals that you use in everyday life.

6. Circle the words that tell what the locals <u>exhibited</u> toward Donnie. Tell about a time someone *exhibited* this type of behavior toward you.

7. Underline the words that tell what <u>outcome</u> Donnie wondered about. If this story continued, what do you think might be the *outcome*?

8. Circle the word that tells who might accept a <u>bribe</u>. Use *bribe* in a sentence.

Name _____ Date _____

"Popocatepetl and Ixtlaccihuatl" by Juliet Piggott Wood

Reading: Reread to Look for Connections That Indicate Cause-and-Effect Relationships

A **cause** is an event or situation that produces a result. An **effect** is the result produced. In a story or an essay, each effect may eventually become a cause for the next event. This series of events results in a cause-and-effect chain, which propels the action forward.

As you read, think about the causes and effects of events. If you do not see a clear cause-and-effect relationship in a passage, **reread to look for connections** in the text. Look for words and phrases that identify cause-and-effect relationships, for example, *because, due to, for that reason, therefore,* and *as a result.*

DIRECTIONS: *Read the following sequences of events. Underline any words or phrases that help you identify a cause-and-effect relationship. Then, identify each event as a* cause, *an* effect, *or both* cause and effect.

_____ 1. The Emperor wants Ixtla to rule the empire after he dies.

_____ 2. Therefore, Ixtla becomes more serious and more studious.

_____ 3. Ixtla also studies harder because she has fallen in love.

_____ 4. The Emperor becomes ill.

_____ 5. As a result, he rules the empire less effectively.

_____ 6. Because the empire has grown weaker, enemies are emboldened to surround it.

_____ 7. Because enemies surround the empire, the Emperor commands his warriors to defeat them.

_____ 8. Jealous warriors tell the Emperor that Popo has been killed in battle.

_____ 9. The Emperor tells Ixtla that Popo has died.

_____ 10. Because she is heartbroken and does not want to marry anyone but Popo, Ixtla grows sick and dies.

_____ 11. When Popo learns the circumstances of Ixtla's death, he kills the warriors who lied to the Emperor.

_____ 12. Popo grieves for Ixtla.

_____ 13. Therefore, Popo instructs the warriors to build two pyramids.

_____ 14. Popo stands atop the second pyramid, holding a burning torch.

_____ 15. Over time, the pyramids became mountains.

"Popocatepetl and Ixtlaccihuatl" by Juliet Piggott Wood
Literary Analysis: Legends and Facts

A **legend** is a traditional story about the past. A legend generally starts out as a story based on **fact**—something that can be proved true. Over the course of many generations, however, the story is retold and transformed into fiction. It becomes a legend.

Every culture has its own legends to immortalize real people who were famous in their time. Most legends include these elements:

- a larger-than-life hero or heroine
- fantastic events
- roots, or a basis, in historical facts
- actions and events that reflect the culture that created the legend

A powerful Aztec emperor wants to pass his kingdom on to his daughter, Ixtlaccihuatl, or Ixtla. Ixtla studies hard so that she will be worthy of this role. She loves Popocatepetl, or Popo, a brave and strong warrior in the service of the emperor. The emperor, Ixtla, and Popo are three larger-than-life characters who will form the basis of the legend.

DIRECTIONS: *Read each excerpt from "Popocatepetl and Ixtlaccihuatl." On the line, identify the element or elements of a legend that the passage reflects, and briefly explain how you recognized the element.*

1. The pass through which the Spaniards came to the ancient Tenochtitlan is still there, as are the volcanoes on each side of that pass. Their names have not been changed. The one to the north is Ixtlaccihuatl and the one on the south of the pass is Popocatepetl.

   Element of legend: _____

   Explanation: _____

2. There was once an Aztec Emperor in Tenochtitlan. He was very powerful. Some thought he was wise as well, whilst other doubted his wisdom.

   Element of legend: _____

   Explanation: _____

3. As time went on natural leaders emerged and, of these, undoubtedly Popo was the best. Finally it was he, brandishing his club and shield, who led the great charge of running warriors across the valley, with their enemies fleeing before them.

   Element of legend: _____

   Explanation: _____

4. So Popocatepetl stood there, holding the torch in memory of Ixtlaccihuatl, for the rest of his days.

   The snows came and, as the years went by, the pyramids of stone became high white-capped mountains.

   Element of legend: _____

   Explanation: _____

73

Name _____ Date _____

Vocabulary Builder

Word List

> decreed   unanimous   refute   routed

A. DIRECTIONS: *Read each item, and think about the meaning of the underlined word from the Word List. Then, answer the question, and explain your answer.*

1. The Emperor <u>decreed</u> that the triumphant warrior would marry his daughter. What kind of statement did the Emperor make?

   _____

2. The story would have ended happily if the warriors' support for Popo had been <u>unanimous</u>. What would have been different?

   _____

   _____

3. Had the Emperor been wise, he would have asked whether anyone could <u>refute</u> the warriors' claims. Would anyone have been able to refute the claims?

   _____

   _____

4. The warriors, led by Popo, <u>routed</u> the enemy. Did the battles continue?

   _____

B. DIRECTIONS: *Write the letter of the word that means the same or about the same as the word from the Word List.*

___ 1. decreed
   A. refused   C. ordered
   B. challenged   D. answered

___ 2. refute
   A. disprove   C. plot
   B. mistake   D. banish

___ 3. unanimous
   A. scattered   C. disappointed
   B. compared   D. undisputed

___ 4. routed
   A. cheered   C. slotted
   B. defeated   D. selected

Name _____ Date _____

Support for Writing a Description

Use this chart to take notes as you prepare to write a **description** of Ixtla. Refer to the legend to determine what Ixtla is like. Write down as many details as you can to describe the various aspects of her character. Include verbs and adjectives that appeal to the five senses: sight, touch, taste, smell, and hearing.

Ixtla

Physical appearance:
Attitude and disposition (what Ixtla is like):
How she acts (what Ixtla does):

Now, use your notes to write a draft of a description of the character of Ixtla. Be sure to use vivid verbs and adjectives that will make your description interesting to your readers. Use words that appeal to the senses of sight, touch, taste, smell, and hearing.

Name _____ Date _____

Support for Extend Learning

Research and Technology

As you do research for a **brief report** on volcanoes in Mexico, use this chart.

Name	Location	Type	Most Recent Eruption	Nearby Human Activity

Listening and Speaking

Respond to the following prompts as you prepare a **persuasive speech** aimed at convincing the Emperor that Popo and Ixtla should be allowed to marry.

Explanation of position: _____

_____

Main points in support of position (solid evidence that will appeal to Emperor's emotions and sense of reason): _____

_____

_____

_____

Phrases that will remind me of my points: _____

_____

_____

Once you have organized your material, transfer your notes to cards that you can refer to as you deliver your speech.

Name _____ Date _____

Enrichment: Volcanoes

A **volcano** is a place in the earth's surface through which molten rock and other materials reach the surface. Deep within the earth, under tremendous pressure and at extreme temperatures, rock exists in the form of hot liquid. That liquid is called **magma.** Magma is constantly moving, and some magma eventually works its way to the surface of the earth. In some places, it works its way through cracks in solid rock. In other places, it reaches the surface by melting the solid rock that lies in its path. When magma reaches the earth's surface, it is **lava.**

Not all volcanic eruptions are alike, and different types of eruptions create different types of volcanoes. There are four major types of volcanoes: cinder cone, composite, shield, and lava dome.

DIRECTIONS: *Do research on the Internet or in a library to find out about the four major kinds of volcanoes. In the second column of the following chart, briefly describe how the volcano forms and what it is made of. In the next column, describe the size and shape of a typical volcano of this type. In the last column, cite the name and location of a famous volcano of the type you have described.*

Types of Volcano	Formation and Composition	Typical Shape and Size	Name and Location of Famous Volcano
Cinder cone			
Composite			
Shield			
Lava dome			

Name _____ Date _____

Build Language Skills: Vocabulary

Denotation and Connotation

A word's **denotation** is the literal meaning, the meaning that appears in a dictionary. A word's **connotations** are the meanings of the word apart from its exact definition; they are the ideas that are associated with the word. (Often a dictionary will provide some clues to a word's connotations, as well.)

Consider the verbs *alter* and *transform,* for example. Both words carry the denotation of "to change." Note that *alter* has the connotation of a slight change, one that does not affect the basic identity of the thing that is changing. *Transform,* however, has the connotation of a major change, such that the basic identity of the thing changes radically.

When you read, paying attention to connotations can help you figure out a work's deeper meaning.

A. DIRECTIONS: *Study each pair of synonyms and their denotation. If you are unsure of the words' connotations, consult a dictionary. Then, complete the sentences that follow by writing the correct synonym.*

resolute, obstinate: determined

1. Ixtla was _____ in her commitment to the Emperor's wishes.
2. The Emperor was _____ in his wish that his daughter not marry.

excited, agitated: stirred up; aroused

3. When Ixtla heard that Popo had died, she became _____.
4. When the warriors routed the enemy, they were happy and _____.

Academic Vocabulary Practice

B. DIRECTIONS: *Read each sentence, and think about the meaning of the underlined Academic Vocabulary word. Then, answer the question, and explain your answer.*

1. What might be an <u>effect</u> of a long-term drought?

_____

2. How might a drought <u>affect</u> a region?

_____

3. What might be the <u>consequence</u> of contracting a virus?

_____

4. What might <u>occur</u> if warring nations call for a truce?

_____

5. Why might you <u>alter</u> the route you take to school?

_____

Name _____ Date _____

"Tenochtitlan: Inside the Aztec Capital" by Jacqueline Dineen
"Popocatepetl and Ixtlaccihuatl" by Juliet Piggott Wood
Build Language Skills: Grammar

Commas and Semicolons
A **comma** (,) is used in the following ways:

Function	Example
to separate two independent clauses that are joined by a conjunction	One mountain is called Popocatepetl, and the other one is called Ixtlaccihuatl.
to separate three or more words, phrases, or clauses in a series	There were goblets for pulque and other drinks, graters for grinding chills, and storage pots of various designs.
after an introductory word, phrase, or clause	Unfortunately, some warriors were jealous of Popo. On an island in a swampy lake, the Aztecs built a city. As the city grew, more and more land was drained.

The **semicolon** (;) looks like a period above a comma. It has two main uses:

Function	Example
to join independent clauses that are not joined by a conjunction	One mountain is called Popocatepetl; the other one is called Ixtlaccihuatl.
to separate items in a series when one or more of the items itself contains a comma	The three main characters in the legend are the Emperor; his daughter, Ixtla; and Popo, a warrior.

A. PRACTICE: *Each sentence is missing one or more commas or semicolons. Rewrite each sentence with the correct punctuation.*

1. The family consisted of a couple their married children and their grandchildren.

   _____

2. Aztec houses were very plain everyone slept on mats of reeds.

   _____

B. Writing Application: *Write two sentences about the Aztecs. In one, use one or more semicolons, and in the other, use one or more commas.*

   _____

   _____

   _____

"Popocatepetl and Ixtlaccihuatl" by Juliet Piggott Wood
Selection Test A

Critical Reading *Identify the letter of the choice that best answers the question.*

____ 1. What people does the legend "Popocatepetl and Ixtlaccihuatl" tell about?
  A. the Mexicans
  B. the Spaniards
  C. the Texcocoan
  D. the Aztec

____ 2. According to "Popocatapetl and Ixtlaccihuatl," why is Ixtlaccihuatl called The White Woman?
  A. The peak of the volcano is in the clouds.
  B. The peak of the volcano is covered with snow.
  C. The peak of the volcano has white flowers on it.
  D. The peak of the volcano has white sheep grazing on it.

____ 3. Which of the following sentences from "Popocatapetl and Ixtlaccihuatl" uses a word or phrase that signals a cause-and-effect relationship?
  A. It is not known for how many years the Emperor ruled in Tenochtitlan.
  B. She was a dutiful daughter and learned all she could from her father.
  C. She had a pleasant disposition, and, as a result, she had many friends.
  D. An emperor, they felt, who was not truly wise could not also be truly great.

____ 4. In "Popocatepetl and Ixtlaccihuatl," which of these events causes Ixtla to become more studious and serious?
  I.   She realizes her great responsibilities.
  II. She discovers that parties are boring.
  III. She realizes that her father is not wise.
  IV. She falls in love with Popocatepetl.
  A. I and III
  B. II and IV
  C. I and IV
  D. II and III

____ 5. According to "Popocatepetl and Ixtlaccihuatl," why does the Emperor at first refuse to let Ixtlaccihuatl marry Popocatepetl?
  A. He does not like or trust Popo.
  B. He wants Ixtla to marry someone else.
  C. He wants Popo to lead the army.
  D. He wants Ixtla to remain single.

_____ 6. According to "Popocatepetl and Ixtlaccihuatl," why is Ixtla fearful when she hears of her father's bribe?

A. She knows he is near death.

B. She wants to marry only Popo.

C. She does not want to be Empress.

D. She has disguised herself as a warrior.

_____ 7. Which emotion causes Popo to act as he does at the end of "Popocatepetl and Ixtlaccihuatl"?

A. confusion

B. wisdom

C. joy

D. grief

_____ 8. Which element of a legend do the characters Popo and Ixtla most obviously represent?

A. larger-than-life human beings

B. a fantastic, unrealistic occurrence

C. a historical fact

D. Aztec culture

_____ 9. Which of the following adjectives best describes the Emperor in "Popocatepetl and Ixtlaccihuatl?"

A. selfish

B. courageous

C. loving

D. wise

_____ 10. At the end of "Popocatepetl and Ixtlaccihuatl," two pyramids turn into volcanic mountains. Which element of a legend does the transformation most clearly represent?

A. larger-than-life human beings

B. a fantastic, unrealistic occurrence

C. a historical fact

D. Aztec culture

_____ 11. Which statement best reflects the conclusion of "Popocatepetl and Ixtlaccihuatl"?

A. Revenge leads to death.

B. Soldiers are ambitious.

C. True love lasts long after death.

D. Wars do not bring lasting peace.

Vocabulary and Grammar

___ 12. Which sentence demonstrates the meaning of the word *unanimous*?

A. The Emperor demanded that Popo's body be brought home.

B. All the warriors agreed that Popo had led them to victory.

C. Ixtla felt so much sorrow that she became ill and died.

D. Popo honored Ixtla by holding a torch in her memory.

___ 13. In which sentence is the comma or commas used correctly?

A. Ixtla was beautiful, dutiful, and serious.

B. Ixtla, honored her father, but wanted to marry Popo.

C. Popo was a great warrior, he led the Aztecs to victory.

D. Popo built a pyramid, to honor Ixtla.

___ 14. In which sentence is the semicolon used correctly?

A. The Emperor was powerful; but he was not wise.

B. The Emperor was powerful; he won many battles.

C. Popo and Ixtla live forever; and the volcanoes bear their names.

D. These are the names of the volcanoes; Popocatepetl and Ixtlaccihuatl.

Essay

15. In "Popocatepetl and Ixtlaccihuatl," Ixtla and Popo fall in love. Are they well suited to each other? In an essay, describe each character. Tell what does or does not make him or her a good match for the other. Cite one detail about each character to support your opinion.

16. In "Popocatepetl and Ixtlaccihuatl," Popo becomes angry with the warriors who lied to the Emperor and thereby cause Ixtla's death. He responds by challenging them to combat, and he kills each one What do you think of Popo's response? Were the warriors responsible for Ixtla's death? How else might Popo have behaved? In an essay, describe your reaction to Popo's behavior. If you believe it was just, explain why. If you believe it was unjust, explain why, and suggest a response that would have been more appropriate.

"Popocatepetl and Ixtlaccihuatl" by Juliet Piggott Wood
Selection Test B

Critical Reading *Identify the letter of the choice that best completes the statement or answers the question.*

____ 1. What people does the legend "Popocatepetl and Ixtlaccihuatl" tell about?
A. the Aztecs living before the Spanish conquest
B. the Aztecs living after the Spanish conquest
C. the Spanish at the time of the conquest
D. the residents of Mexico City today

____ 2. In "Popocatepetl and Ixtlaccihuatl," about what did the Aztec people disagree?
A. whether the Emperor was brave
B. whether the Emperor was powerful
C. whether the Emperor was wise
D. whether the Emperor was handsome

____ 3. According to "Popocatepetl and Ixtlaccihuatl," Ixtla studies hard in order to succeed her father. That information suggests that Ixtla is
A. dutiful.
B. reluctant.
C. friendly.
D. romantic.

____ 4. In "Popocatepetl and Ixtlaccihuatl," what characteristic does the Emperor show when he refuses to let Ixtla marry Popo?
A. thoughtfulness
B. selfishness
C. sincerity
D. reluctance

____ 5. According to "Popocatepetl and Ixtlaccihuatl," an Emperor who is not wise cannot be
A. elected.
B. defeated.
C. happy.
D. great.

____ 6. "Popocatepetl and Ixtlaccihuatl" tells how the Emperor falls ill. What happens as a result?
A. Popo and Ixtla get married.
B. The Empress begins to rule.
C. The warriors leave the kingdom.
D. Enemies surround the capital.

____ 7. According to "Popocatepetl and Ixtlaccihuatl," what causes the warriors to lie about Popo's death?
A. ignorance
B. jealousy
C. pride
D. fear

____ 8. Based on "Popocatepetl and Ixtlaccihuatl," what can you conclude about the Emperor when he believes the warriors' lies about Popo?
A. He does not want Ixtla to marry Popo.
B. He is naive and too quick to trust.
C. He is too sorrowful to think sensibly.
D. He does not want Ixtla to marry at all.

____ 9. According to "Popocatepetl and Ixtlaccihuatl," Ixtla dies of a broken heart. What is another way to describe the cause of her death?
A. the flu
B. a heart attack
C. severe grief
D. a stroke

____ 10. At the end of "Popocatepetl and Ixtlaccihuatl," what do the two volcanoes symbolize?
A. temples
B. lovers
C. burial mounds
D. buried cities

____ 11. Which statement best reflects the conclusion of "Popocatepetl and Ixtlaccihuatl"?
A. There can be no revenge.
B. Ambition is its own reward.
C. True love outlasts death.
D. War breeds only war.

____ 12. Why might the volcanoes Popocatepetl and Ixtlaccihuatl have been the subject of an Aztec legend?
A. They erupted constantly.
B. They appeared suddenly.
C. They were part of the landscape.
D. They attraced wealthy tourists.

____ 13. Which element of "Popocatepetl and Ixtlaccihuatl" is most obviously based on fact?
A. the volcanoes
B. the Emperor
C. Popo and Ixtla
D. the warriors

_____ **14.** In what way is "Popocatepetl and Ixtlaccihuatl" characteristic of a legend?
  A. It is a fantastic narrative about someone's ancestors.
  B. It is a narrative about larger-than-life human beings.
  C. It is a narrative featuring animal characters.
  D. It is a factual narrative about the past.

Vocabulary and Grammar

_____ **15.** Which sentence expresses the meaning of the word *decreed*?
  A. The Aztec warriors marched on their enemies.
  B. Ixtla studied hard to learn to be a good ruler.
  C. The Emperor ordered that Popo's body be brought back.
  D. For the rest of his life, Popo stood on a pyramid holding a torch.

_____ **16.** Which sentence expresses the meaning of the word *refute*?
  A. The liars knew that the other men would prove them wrong.
  B. The tribes outside Tenochtitlan began to surround the city.
  C. Ixtla decided that she would die rather than live without Popo.
  D. The Emperor said that the winning warrior might marry Ixtla.

_____ **17.** In which sentence is the comma used correctly?
  A. The warriors defeated the Aztec enemies, the Emperor was happy.
  B. When the Emperor was in his middle years, his daughter was born.
  C. Popo had two pyramids built, one was for him and one was for Ixtla.
  D. Popo and Ixtla fell in love, the Emperor refused to allow them to marry.

_____ **18.** In which sentence is the semicolon used correctly?
  A. Popo challenged the liars to fight him; no one tried to stop him.
  B. The enemies of the Aztecs surrounded the city; and they waited for dawn to break.
  C. Popo and Ixtla continued to see one another; but they were not permitted to marry.
  D. The Emperor showed that he was unwise; not letting Popo and Ixtla marry.

Essay

19. Based on "Popocatepetl and Ixtlaccihuatl," what can you conclude about the place of women in Aztec society? In an essay, tell what you know about women in Aztec society. Cite three details from the selection to support your statements.

20. Based on your reading of "Popocatepetl and Ixtlaccihuatl," what can you conclude about the traits the Aztecs admired? Consider the Emperor, Ixtla, Popo, and the warriors who lied. Which of their characteristics were held in high esteem? Which were not? In an essay, describe the characteristics the Aztecs seem to have found most worthy. Cite at least three examples from the selection.

21. "Popocatepetl and Ixtlaccihuatl" contains many references to Aztec history, culture, and traditions. However, the legend also has universal appeal. In an essay, discuss the aspects of the legend that might appeal to people in any culture at any time. Cite three examples from the selection to support your points.

Vocabulary Warm-up Word Lists

Study these words from the selections. Then, complete the activities.

Word List A

fortunately [FAWR chuhn it lee] *adv.* luckily
  <u>Fortunately</u>, Madison had remembered her umbrella.

glittering [GLIT er ing] *adj.* sparkling
  The <u>glittering</u> decorations transformed the gym into a dance floor.

hideous [HID ee uhs] *adj.* extremely ugly
  Ethan wore a <u>hideous</u> outfit of green shorts and a bright plaid shirt.

horrible [HAWR uh buhl] *adj.* frightful; causing horror
  Emma let out a <u>horrible</u> scream when she saw the accident.

invisible [in VIZ uh buhl] *adj.* not able to be seen
  The wind was <u>invisible</u>, but its effects were not.

marble [MAHR buhl] *adj.* made of a hard, crystallized limestone
  Jacob bought a <u>marble</u> statue for the back yard.

sandals [SAN duhlz] *n.* open shoes held to the feet by straps
  Olivia wore a summer dress and a pair of leather <u>sandals</u>.

slay [SLAY] *v.* to kill, especially by violence
  The soldier did not want to <u>slay</u> anyone, unless in self-defense.

Word List B

afterward [AF ter werd] *adv.* at a later time
  Hannah went to the movies; <u>afterward</u>, she met Jean for lunch.

confident [KAHN fi duhnt] *adj.* feeling certain; sure
  Having studied hard, Pam is <u>confident</u> that she will pass the test.

hissing [HIS ing] *adj.* making prolonged sounds like *ss*
  The <u>hissing</u> animal was warning us to stay away.

petrified [PET ruh fyd] *adj.* like stone
  Tyler brought back a piece of <u>petrified</u> wood from the forest.

regret [ri GRET] *v.* to feel sorry about
  The girls <u>regret</u> that they neglected to invite Simone to the party.

serpents [SER puhnts] *n.* snakes, especially large ones
  Cole enjoys looking at the <u>serpents</u> at the zoo.

spectator [SPEK tay ter] *n.* a person who sees or watches
  Abby was a <u>spectator</u> at the Olympic swimming events.

utterly [UT er lee] *adv.* completely; totally
  Kayla was <u>utterly</u> embarrassed when she slipped and fell.

"Perseus" by Alice Low
"Percy-Us Brings the Gawgon's Head" by Lloyd Alexander
Vocabulary Warm-up Exercises

Exercise A *Fill in each blank in the paragraph below with an appropriate word from Word List A. Use each word only once.*

Lydia was tired of watching the news. It was awful to hear how various armies

continued to [1] _____ one another on distant battlefields. She

thought it was just [2] _____ that their leaders couldn't come to some

agreements and stop the fighting. She decided to relax for a while in the garden.

[3] _____ for Lydia, all the gardening chores for the week had already

been done. She sat down on the [4] _____ bench that her father had put

in the garden last year. She gazed at the fountain with its [5] _____

water lit by the sun. She removed her [6] _____ so she could enjoy the

feel of the grass on her feet. She watched with wonder as a spider wove an almost

[7] _____ web in the tree. Despite the fact that she was wearing a

[8] _____, old patched skirt that hurt even her own eyes, Lydia felt good.

Exercise B *Revise each sentence so that the underlined vocabulary word is used in a logical way. Be sure to keep the vocabulary word in your revision.*

Example: Samantha was <u>utterly</u> surprised when the sun came up in the morning.
Samantha was <u>utterly</u> surprised when her uncle gave her a new laptop.

1. Dean dried off, using a big, white towel; <u>afterward</u>, he took a shower.

   _____

2. You can tell that Candace is <u>confident</u> because she nervously bites her nails.

   _____

3. The calm cat, <u>hissing</u> at the dog, was obviously content and relaxed.

   _____

4. The <u>petrified</u> trees were covered with new growth.

   _____

5. Carly and Jesse <u>regret</u> that they studied enough for the exam.

   _____

6. Because the <u>serpents</u> were near, the mice were not in any danger.

   _____

7. As a <u>spectator</u> at the football game, Matt wore a helmet and other protective gear.

   _____

Name _____   Date _____

Read the following passage. Pay special attention to the underlined words. Then, read it again, and complete the activities. Use a separate sheet of paper for your written answers.

The Greek myth about Perseus and Andromeda is an interesting one. Perseus was flying home, wearing on his feet the winged sandals that Hermes had given him. No one could see him, for he was invisible. He was wearing Hermes's other gift, an invisibility cap. Flying over Ethiopia, he looked down and saw a beautiful young woman chained to a rock. She was wearing only a few pieces of glittering jewelry. At first, Perseus thought she was a marble statue, but when he saw her tears, he knew she was alive.

He removed his invisibility cap and spoke to her. "Who are you? Why are you bound to this rock by those chains?"

"I am Andromeda," she said, "daughter of Cepheus, the King of Ethiopia. My mother is Queen Cassiopeia. Some time ago, my mother, proud of her beauty and of mine, dared to say that we were more beautiful than the sea nymphs. They went to Poseidon, the god of the sea, and demanded vengeance for my mother's insult. Poseidon sent a hideous sea monster with breath of fire to attack our coast and destroy our villages. The oracle told my father that the only way to stop the destruction was to offer me as a sacrifice to the sea monster."

"Fortunately," said Perseus, "I can save you! If I could kill Medusa, I can surely slay a sea monster."

Then, Perseus heard a horrible sound from the water. The sea monster was approaching, breathing fire and roaring loudly. Perseus soared into the air. He pounced on the sea monster's back and plunged his sword between the scales time and time again. At last, the monster was dead.

Perseus then released Andromeda from her chains, and she agreed to marry him. Her parents were joyful. All over the land, the people rejoiced.

1. Circle the words that tell where Perseus wore the winged sandals that Hermes had given him. Use the word *sandals* in a sentence.

2. Underline the words that suggest the meaning of invisible. Name an *invisible* force or quality that affects you in everyday life.

3. Circle the word that is described as glittering. What does *glittering* mean?

4. Underline the word that marble describes. Name three other materials besides *marble* that might be used for a statue.

5. Underline the words that are described as hideous. If someone described a jacket as *hideous*, what might it look like?

6. Circle the words that Perseus describes as fortunately. What is another word that means about the same as *fortunately*?

7. Circle the word that means about the same as slay. Use *slay* in a sentence.

8. Circle the words in a nearby sentence that further describe the horrible sound that Perseus heard. What does *horrible* mean?

"Perseus" by Alice Low
"Percy-Us Brings the Gawgon's Head" by Lloyd Alexander
Reading Warm-up B

Read the following passage. Pay special attention to the underlined words. Then, read it again, and complete the activities. Use a separate sheet of paper for your written answers.

In Greek mythology, the Gorgons were winged female monsters. Their mother was Ceto, and their father was Phorcys, son of the Sea and the Earth. Two of the Gorgons, Stheno and Euryale, were immortal. The third, Medusa, was mortal. This meant that she could die. These sisters had all been beautiful at one time. However, they had been changed into hideous, ugly monsters. Ancient art portrays them as having <u>serpents</u> in place of hair. They also had very long tongues. Their teeth were bigger than those of a wild boar. Their stare would turn any <u>spectator</u> who looked at them into a <u>petrified</u> statue.

The story of Medusa is tragic. She started out as a beautiful woman who had many suitors. Her greatest pride was her long, silky hair. Medusa knew she was as beautiful as any goddess. She was so attractive that even the goddess Athena was jealous of her.

One day, Poseidon, the god of the sea, fell in love with Medusa after spotting her in one of Athena's temples. This made Athena so angry that she changed Medusa into a horrible creature whose hair was a swarm of <u>hissing</u> snakes.

<u>Afterward</u>, Medusa lived in a cavern with her two sisters. That cavern was full of the stony statues of the animals and men who had been unfortunate enough to see them.

Most images of Medusa in art show her as an <u>utterly</u> frightening, hideous creature, full of rage. However, a few other works portray her with a beautiful, sorrowful face surrounded by intertwined snakes that are growing out of her head. This type of art reminds the viewer that Medusa was, at one time, lovely. The tragedy of her life was that she was too <u>confident</u> of her own beauty. Athena's punishment made Medusa forever <u>regret</u> that she had dared to compare herself to a goddess.

1. Underline the word that tells what part of Medusa's body the <u>serpents</u> replaced. Give a synonym for **serpents**.

2. Circle the words that tell what a <u>spectator</u> might do. Describe a time you were a **spectator**.

3. Underline the word that is described as <u>petrified</u>. Use **petrified** in a sentence.

4. Circle the word that tells what was <u>hissing</u>. What does **hissing** mean?

5. Athena turned Medusa's hair to a swarm of snakes. Underline the words that tell what happened <u>afterward</u>. Describe a fun activity you did with a friend. Then tell what you did **afterward**.

6. Circle the word that is described as <u>utterly</u>. Use **utterly** in a sentence.

7. Underline the words that tell what made Medusa feel so <u>confident</u>. What makes you feel **confident**?

8. Circle the words that tell what Athena's punishment made Medusa <u>regret</u>. Name one thing that you **regret**.

Name _____ Date _____

"Perseus" by Alice Low
"Percy-Us Brings the Gawgon's Head" by Lloyd Alexander
Literary Analysis: Comparing Treatment of Epic Conventions

An **epic** is a story or long poem about the adventures of a larger-than-life hero. The hero's parents are often gods or members of a royal family. Epic tales usually focus on the hero's bravery, strength, and success in battle or adventure. In addition to telling the story of a hero, an epic is a portrait of the culture that produced it. The following **epic conventions** are traditional characteristics of this form of literature:

- An epic involves a dangerous journey, or *quest*, that the hero must take.
- Gods or powerful characters help the hero.
- The setting of an epic is broad, covering several nations or even the universe.
- The style is serious and formal.

Because epics have become an important part of the literature of different cultures, they often inspire the works of later generations. The new works may vary widely. For example, one modern author based an ambitious novel on the ancient Greek epic the *Odyssey*, while another has used the epic to tell a humorous tale. As you read "Perseus" and "Percy-Us Brings the Gawgon's Head," determine which story is closer to the original epic and which was written to make you chuckle.

DIRECTIONS: *Use the following chart to compare "Perseus" and "Percy-Us Brings the Gawgon's Head." If the information to answer a question does not appear in the selection, write* information not mentioned.

Questions	"Perseus"	"Percy-Us Brings the Gawgon's Head"
1. What is the setting?		
2. Who is the hero?		
3. Who are the hero's parents?		
4. What dangerous journey must the hero undertake?		
5. Who helps the hero in his quest?		
6. What is the creature like that the hero must face?		
7. What does each hero accomplish?		
8. Which story is closer to the original? Which is humorous?		

"Perseus" by Alice Low
"Percy-Us Brings the Gawgon's Head" by Lloyd Alexander
Vocabulary Builder

Word List

cowered	hideous	pursuit	knack	reveling	pathetic	petrified

A. DIRECTIONS: *Think about the meaning of each italicized word from the Word List. Then, explain whether the sentence makes sense. If it does not make sense, write a new sentence. In the new sentence, use the italicized word correctly.*

1. Everyone admired the *hideous* dress.

   Explanation: _____

   New sentence: _____

2. My family visited a *petrified* forest to see trees that had turned to rock.

   Explanation: _____

   New sentence: _____

3. The children were in *pursuit* of their mother as they waited on the front porch.

   Explanation: _____

   New sentence: _____

4. The dog *cowered* under the table during the fierce thunderstorm.

   Explanation: _____

   New sentence: _____

B. DIRECTIONS: *Write the letter of the word or group of words whose meaning is* most opposite *that of the vocabulary word.*

____ 1. knack
   A. noise
   B. lack of noise
   C. talent
   D. lack of talent

____ 2. pathetic
   A. admirable
   B. pitiful
   C. foolish
   D. tolerant

____ 3. reveling
   A. exposing
   B. waiting
   C. mourning
   D. hiding

Name _____ Date _____

"Perseus" by Alice Low
"Percy-Us Brings the Gawgon's Head" by Lloyd Alexander
Support for Writing to Compare Literary Works

Use this graphic organizer to take notes for an **essay** in which you compare and contrast the heroes Perseus and Percy-Us.

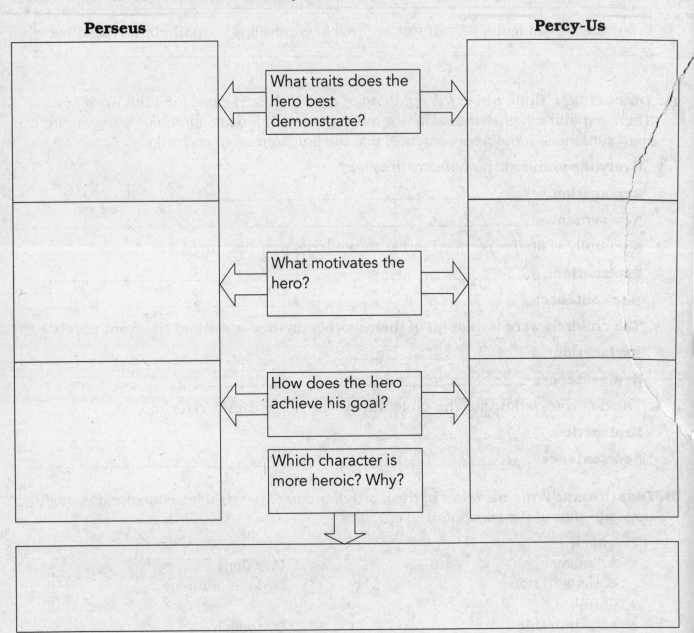

Perseus   **Percy-Us**

What traits does the hero best demonstrate?

What motivates the hero?

How does the hero achieve his goal?

Which character is more heroic? Why?

Now, use your notes to write an essay comparing and contrasting the heroes Perseus and Percy-Us.

"**Perseus**" by Alice Low
"**Percy-Us Brings the Gawgon's Head**" by Lloyd Alexander
Selection Test A

Critical Reading *Identify the letter of the choice that best answers the question.*

___ 1. In "Perseus," what does Acrisius do when he learns that his daughter has had a son?
A. He locks them in an underground bronze house.
B. He has them locked in a large wooden chest and thrown into the sea.
C. He sends them away to a small island.
D. He sends them to the three Gorgons, hoping that the Gorgons will kill them.

___ 2. According to "Perseus," who helps Perseus by giving him weapons and telling him how he can kill Medusa?
A. Polydectes
B. Danaë and Dictys
C. Hermes and Athena
D. King Acrisius

___ 3. In "Perseus," why does Perseus take the eye that is being shared by the three Gray Women?
A. so that they will tell him where to find the nymphs of the North
B. so that they will tell him the secret of how to kill the Gorgon
C. so that he can use the eye to look at Medusa and defeat her
D. so that he can play a joke on them in return for their shaming him

___ 4. In "Perseus," why does Perseus have to look into the shield when he is cutting off the head of Medusa?
A. Medusa is invisible, and the shield lets Perseus see her.
B. If he looks directly at Medusa, the look in her eyes will blind him.
C. He does not want Medusa to see the fear on his face.
D. If he looks directly at Medusa's face, he will be turned to stone.

___ 5. In "Percy-Us Brings the Gawgon's Head," what is The Gawgon doing when Percy-Us arrives?
A. sleeping on the ground
B. sitting in a rocking chair
C. eating her lunch
D. fighting with the other Gawgons

___ 6. In "Percy-Us Brings the Gawgon's Head," why does Percy-Us have such a hard time cutting off The Gawgon's head?

    A. The snakes that are The Gawgon's hair keep moving around and hiding her neck.

    B. The Gawgon keeps talking to him as he tries to use the sword.

    C. He is looking into the reflection from his shield and confuses his left and his right.

    D. The sword is heavy and the shield is big, so he cannot hold both at the same time.

___ 7. In "Percy-Us Brings the Gawgon's Head," why does The Gawgon come up with a plan to help Percy-Us?

    A. because Percy-Us forces her to

    B. so that Percy-Us will not cut off her head

    C. because she is in love with Percy-Us

    D. so that Percy-Us will do her a favor

___ 8. In "Percy-Us Brings the Gawgon's Head," what happens with the promise that Percy-Us has made to Polly Deck-Tease?

    A. He brings the whole Gawgon, which includes the head, and so keeps the promise.

    B. He keeps the promise by bringing the Gawgon's severed head.

    C. He decides that Polly Deck-Tease does not want him to keep his promise.

    D. He decides that Polly Deck-Tease has been using him, so he will not keep the promise.

___ 9. How is the image of Percy-Us flying different from the image of Perseus flying?

    A. Percy-Us does not know how to land.

    B. Percy-Us flies with the help of Hermes.

    C. Percy-Us flies upside down and backward.

    D. Percy-Us has to hold The Gawgon's hand.

___ 10. How do Perseus and Percy-Us differ in their use of a sword?

    A. Perseus is accurate; Percy-Us keeps missing.

    B. Perseus misses several times; Percy-Us is accurate.

    C. Perseus cannot lift the sword; Percy-Us lifts it easily.

    D. Perseus misses every time; Percy-Us is successful on his third try.

___ 11. How is the fate of Medusa the Gorgon different from the fate of The Gawgon?

    A. Medusa survives undefeated.

    B. Medusa is turned to stone.

    C. Medusa talks Perseus out of killing her.

    D. Medusa has her head cut off.

_____ **12.** How does the style of "Perseus" compare with the style of "Percy-Us Brings the Gawgon's Head"?

    A. "Perseus" is more formal.

    B. "Perseus" is more humorous.

    C. "Percy-Us" is more serious.

    D. "Percy-Us" is more informative.

Vocabulary

_____ **13.** How would you describe a person who is *reveling*?

    A. sad

    B. angry

    C. dizzy

    D. joyful

_____ **14.** What would you think about a *pathetic* person?

    A. He or she should be pitied.

    B. He or she should have a lot of friends.

    C. He or she should do well in school.

    D. He or she should work hard all the time.

_____ **15.** What would you expect from person with a *knack*?

    A. He or she would travel a lot.

    B. He or she would find success at something.

    C. He or she would have to have an operation.

    D. He or she would get into trouble often.

Essay

16. Two very different heroes are presented in "Perseus" and "Percy-Us Brings the Gawgon's Head." In an essay, compare and contrast the scene in each selection in which the hero attempts to cut off the monster's head. What does Perseus do? How is he successful? What does Percy-Us do? How is he successful? Is one hero more successful than the other? Explain your answer.

17. In both "Perseus" and "Percy-Us Brings the Gawgon's Head," the hero faces a monster. In an essay, compare and contrast the appearance of Medusa the Gorgon and The Gawgon. Tell what each character looks like. Is there any way in which they are alike? How are they different? In your essay, cite at least two details from each selection.

"Perseus" by Alice Low
"Percy-Us Brings the Gawgon's Head" by Lloyd Alexander
Selection Test B

Critical Reading *Identify the letter of the choice that best completes the statement or answers the question.*

____ 1. According to "Perseus," why does King Acrisius lock his daughter and grandson in a wooden chest and throw them into the sea?
  A. The king is jealous of his grandson's strength and good looks.
  B. An oracle has told the king his grandson would kill him.
  C. The king wanted a son and not a daughter.
  D. His grandson is the son of Zeus, whom he dislikes.

____ 2. Why does Polydectes ask Perseus to bring him the head of Medusa?
  A. He knows that Perseus is brave enough to kill the terrible monster.
  B. He wants to reward Perseus but wants Perseus to prove himself first.
  C. He wants Perseus to die and expects that the monster will kill him.
  D. He hopes Perseus will refuse to kill the monster and look like a coward.

____ 3. Why must Perseus go to see the Gray Women?
  A. to find out where the nymphs of the North live
  B. to steal their eye and use it to look at the Gorgon
  C. to get the winged sandals, magic wallet, and cap of invisibility
  D. to find out the secret of how to kill the Gorgons

____ 4. In "Percy-Us Brings the Gawgon's Head," why does Percy-Us have trouble flying to the mountains where The Gawgon lives?
  A. The heavy sword and shield he has been given weigh him down.
  B. Birds bump into him because he is wearing the cap of invisibility.
  C. He miscalculates the location of the mountains and gets lost.
  D. He cannot figure out how to stop or land once he starts flying.

____ 5. Why does The Gawgon give Percy-Us a licorice gumdrop?
  A. so that he will get drowsy and fall asleep
  B. so that he will trust her and do what she says
  C. so that he will not have the strength to cut off her head
  D. so that he will be able to look at her without turning to stone

____ 6. What does The Gawgon mean by this line from "Percy-Us Brings the Gawgon's Head"?
  What you promised was at the expense of an innocent bystander who never did you any harm.
  A. The Gawgon is the innocent bystander who is going to be killed because of his promise.
  B. Polly Deck-Tease's innocent wedding guests will be harmed when they see The Gawgon.
  C. Polly Deck-Tease's motives for asking Perseus to kill The Gawgon were innocent.
  D. Hermes is the innocent bystander who will be harmed when he sees The Gawgon.

____ 7. How does Percy-Us keep his word to Polly Deck-Tease?
  A. He brings Polly Deck-Tease The Gawgon's severed head.
  B. He brings Polly Deck-Tease a different severed head.
  C. He brings The Gawgon alive so that she can breathe fire on Polly Deck-Tease.
  D. He brings The Gawgon alive and presents the king with the head.

____ 8. The scene in which Percy-Us flies is different from the scene in which Perseus flies in that
  A. Percy-Us does not know how to land.
  B. Percy-Us must fly with the help of Hermes.
  C. Percy-Us flies upside down and backward at first.
  D. Percy-Us must hold The Gawgon's hand to fly successfully.

____ 9. Perseus's use of a sword differs from Percy-Us's use of a sword in that
  A. Perseus is successful the first time.
  B. Perseus misses several times.
  C. Perseus misses every time.
  D. Perseus cannot lift the sword.

____ 10. Perseus's encounter with the Gorgon is different from Percy-Us's encounter with The Gawgon in that
  A. the Gorgons are waiting for Perseus, but The Gawgon does not expect Percy-Us.
  B. the Gorgons are sleeping, but The Gawgon is rocking in a rocking chair.
  C. the Gorgons are having their dinner, but The Gawgon is sleeping.
  D. the Gorgons are sleeping, but The Gawgon is having lunch.

____ 11. The fate of Medusa is different from the fate of The Gawgon in that
  A. Medusa defeats her enemies.
  B. Medusa is turned to stone.
  C. Medusa talks the hero out of killing her.
  D. Medusa's head is chopped off.

____ 12. How is what happens at Polly Deck-Tease's court different from what happens at Polydectes' court?
  A. In "Percy-Us," the king and his guests are turned to stone.
  B. In "Percy-Us," only the king is turned to stone.
  C. In "Percy-Us," the king does not mock the hero.
  D. In "Percy-Us," the king's guests want to fight the hero.

____ 13. Compared with the style of "Perseus," the style of "Percy-Us Brings the Gawgon's Head" is more
  A. formal.
  B. humorous.
  C. serious.
  D. informative.

Vocabulary

____ 14. In which sentence does *hideous* make sense?
   A. Sheila is a *hideous* girl because she is not too short and not too tall.
   B. Kevin wrote an essay about his *hideous* vacation on a beautiful tropical island.
   C. The *hideous* monster seemed so real that everyone in the movie theater screamed.
   D. The beginning of the story was *hideous* to read because it was slow and boring.

____ 15. Which sentence describes a *pathetic* situation?
   A. A hero trembles at the sight of a mouse.
   B. A child falls down in the playground.
   C. A bride looks beautiful at her wedding.
   D. A king attends a sporting event.

____ 16. Which sentence best expresses the meaning of *knack*?
   A. The king had carpenters build a large wooden chest.
   B. Fishermen are often out at sea by daybreak.
   C. Perseus realizes that Polydectes wanted him to die.
   D. Heroes have a talent for slaying frightening monsters.

____ 17. In which sentences is the subject most likely *reveling*?
   A. Jen learns that her favorite TV show was canceled.
   B. Charlie is going to meet Shannon and Mark at the library.
   C. Jake is surrounded by his friends at a surprise birthday party.
   D. Maya is starting a new job as soon as the school year ends.

Essay

18. In both "Perseus" and "Percy-Us Brings the Gawgon's Head," a hero is presented. In an essay, compare and contrast Perseus and Percy-Us. Name at least one way in which they are alike and at least two ways in which they different. Then, tell whether you found one of the characters more "heroic." Cite at least one detail from one of the selections to support your point.

19. An epic is a story or long poem about the adventures of a larger-than-life hero. An epic may be distinguished by these traditional characteristics:

   • It involves a dangerous journey, or quest.
   • The hero receives help from gods or powerful characters.
   • The events unfold in at least several nations.
   • The story is told in a serious, formal style

In an essay, discuss those characteristics in terms of "Perseus" and "Percy-Us Brings the Gawgon's Head." To what extent are they present in "Perseus"? To what extent are they present in "Percy-Us Brings the Gawgon's Head"? Conclude your essay by stating whether you think "Percy-Us" may be considered an epic. Cite at least one reason to support your opinion.

Name _____ Date _____

Letter: Business Letter

Prewriting: Gathering Details

Complete the following chart to keep track of the information for your letter.

Purpose for Writing	Your Contact Information	Your Recipient's Information	Details to Support Your Request

Drafting: Providing Elaboration

Use the following graphic organizer to develop the body of your business letter by filling in the appropriate information on the right.

Introduction	
Supporting Detail 1	
Supporting Detail 2	
Supporting Detail 3	
Closing/Thank You	

Writing Workshop—Unit 6, Part 1

Business Letter: Integrating Grammar Skills

Revising Incorrect Use of Commas

A **comma** signals a brief pause. You should use a comma in these situations:

before a conjunction that separates two independent clauses in a compound sentence	Our library is full of books, but it also has many other materials.
between items in a series	The library offers pages, tapes and DVDs.
between adjectives of equal rank that modify the same noun or pronoun (If the word *and* can replace the comma, the adjectives are of equal rank)	The old library was a large, ugly building.
to set off introductory words, phrases, or clauses	Entering the library, you turn left for fiction.
to set off words, phrases, and clauses that interrupt a sentence	Mrs. Lee, the librarian, is very helpful.

Identifying Correct Use of Commas

A. DIRECTIONS: *Circle the letter of the sentence that uses commas correctly.*

1. A. The library offers separate sections for fiction, nonfiction, and reference.

   B. The library offers separate sections for fiction, nonfiction and reference.

2. A. In addition, there are separate sections for children and young adults.

   B. In addition there are separate sections for children, and young adults.

3. A. When Mr. Van my neighbor, visits the library he researches his family tree.

   B. When Mr. Van, my neighbor, visits the library, he researches his family tree.

Fixing Incorrect Use of Commas

B. DIRECTIONS: *Rewrite this paragraph with commas inserted or removed wherever necessary.*

After the federal government cut money to the states most state county and local governments had budget problems. Many libraries, and other local services had to be cut back. Hoping to help a group of people began Bookworms an organization that is raising funds for the local library. One of the first things Bookworms organized, was an art show. Many creative, talented, artists donated their works and the money from the sales went to the library.

Unit 6: Themes in the Oral Tradition
Part 1 Benchmark Test 11

MULTIPLE CHOICE

Reading Skill: Cause and Effect

1. Which of the following is an event or action that makes something else happen?
   A. a cause
   B. an effect
   C. a result
   D. a cause-and-effect relationship

2. Which statement best describes a story arranged in a cause-and-effect order?
   A. A single important event in the story is the cause of many events.
   B. Many events in the story are all causes of a single important event.
   C. A story event causes another event, which causes another event, and so on.
   D. Events that are causes are completely unrelated to events that are effects.

3. Which of the following words or phrases signals an effect?
   A. because
   B. since
   C. due to
   D. as a result

Read this brief selection. Then, answer the questions about it.

This winter there had snowstorms late in the season. Because the temperatures remained cold, snow piled high on the ground. Then, due to a sudden warm spell, the snow in our yard melted all at once. There was no place for the water to go except our basement. For this reason, we had more flooding than usual.

4. Which question would best help you identify the cause-and-effect relationships in this selection?
   A. What causes snowstorms late in the season?
   B. At what temperature does water turn to ice?
   C. What happened as a result of the sudden warm spell?
   D. What effects can flooding have on people's homes?

5. Which word or phrase in the selection signals an effect?
   A. because
   B. due to
   C. all at once
   D. for this reason

6. Based on the selection, what caused the snow to pile high on the ground?
   A. a sudden warm spell
   B. cold temperatures
   C. snow plows and shovels
   D. water in the basement

7. Based on the selection, what was the effect of the snow melting all at once?
   A. a sudden warm spell
   B. cold temperatures
   C. snow piles on the ground
   D. water in the basement

Reading Skill: Reading Textbooks

8. What is a textbook?
   A. a collection of fiction and nonfiction that teaches while it entertains
   B. a nonfiction work that presents instructional information in a particular subject area
   C. any work that uses charts, diagrams, or illustrations to help teach information
   D. a nonfiction work that presents instructional information in several subject areas

9. When is it most useful to skim a chapter of a textbook?
   A. when you want a general idea of what the chapter is about
   B. when you want to find a key word or idea in the chapter
   C. when you want to find a particular heading in the chapter
   D. when you want to understand cause-and-effect relationships

10. Why do textbooks write some material in boldface or dark print?
   A. to state the topic of a section
   B. to give background information
   C. to highlight key facts or information
   D. to show cause-and-effect relationships

Literary Analysis: Myths and Legends

11. Why were myths created?
   A. to create a body of literature that would stand the test of time
   B. to explain natural occurrences and express beliefs about right and wrong
   C. to show that gods and goddesses are just like human beings
   D. to give enduring fame to heroes and heroines who contributed to the society

12. What is the term used for writing that can be proved true or false?
   A. a myth
   B. a legend
   C. fiction
   D. a fact

13. What is an important difference between a myth and a legend?
   A. Most myths were created centuries ago, while most legends are modern creations.
   B. Myths were passed down orally, while legends were written literature from the start.
   C. Most myths try to explain a natural occurrence, while legends try to record history.
   D. Myths rarely have human characters, while legends feature only human characters.

14. What do most legends and epics have in common?
   A. They are both told in an informal, everyday language.
   B. They usually have a single, narrow setting.
   C. They both usually feature a dangerous journey or quest.
   D. They both reflect the values of the culture that produced them.

Read the selection. Then, answer the questions that follow.

Narcissus, the son of the river god Cephissus, was very handsome. One day he saw his own reflection in a pool of water. Thinking the lovely creature he saw was a water nymph, he fell in love with his own reflection. He kept trying to touch the beautiful creature, but each time he reached into the water, the creature seemed to move away. He finally died in despair and was turned into the flower which bears his name.

15. What does the myth of Narcissus show about gods and goddesses?
    A. They often display human qualities.
    B. They are all very athletic and handsome.
    C. They rarely display strong emotion.
    D. They are protected by all-powerful gods.

16. What main lesson does the myth of Narcissus teach?
    A. People should not waste water.
    B. Good-looking people are often unaware of their appearance.
    C. Too much self-love can be self-destructive.
    D. It is impossible for a human being to understand beauty.

17. What does the myth of Narcissus explain?
    A. the origin of river gods
    B. the cause of reflections in water
    C. the love of water
    D. the origin of a flower

Read this short legend. Then, answer the questions about it.

As a baby, John Henry reached for a hammer. It showed that he would grow up to be a mighty man. Sure enough, when he grew up, John Henry became a steel driver, hammering steel spikes to help build the railroads. He was amazingly strong and quick, driving steel so hard that lightning sometimes came out of his hammer. One day, when he and his fellow workers were building the C&O railroad tunnel in West Virginia, his boss brought a steam drill to the job. Insisting that he was better than any machine, John Henry agreed to race against the steam drill. He beat the steam drill by four feet, but he worked so hard that he died. Millions of admirers came from all over America to attend his funeral.

18. Which of the following details is most likely a fact on which the legend of John Henry is based?
    A. Baby John Henry reached for a hammer to show that he would become a mighty man.
    B. John Henry was a steel driver who helped build the C&O railroad tunnel in West Virginia.
    C. John Henry was so strong and quick that lightning sometimes came out of his hammer.
    D. Millions of people came from all over America to attend John Henry's funeral.

19. What makes John Henry a larger-than-life hero?

    A. He is proud of his job.

    B. He works on the railroad.

    C. He is amazingly strong and quick.

    D. He is helped by gods and goddesses.

20. Based on the details in the selection, what can you conclude about the culture that produced the legend of John Henry?

    A. It was a culture that valued strength hard work.

    B. It was a culture that loved new inventions.

    C. It was a culture that produced strong babies.

    D. It was a culture in which funerals were small, private family affairs.

Literary Analysis: Epics *Read this summary of a famous epic. Then, answer the questions about it.*

Beowulf was the nephew of the king of the Geats, a people who lived in what is now Sweden. As a young man he won fame for his courage and strength in battle; he was also a fine swimmer and sailor. One day he sailed to nearby Denmark to help the Danes destroy a terrible monster named Grendel, who made nightly raids in which he grabbed Danish people to eat. After killing Grendel, Beowulf had to face Grendel's angry mother, whom he also killed. The Danish king rewarded Beowulf with riches. Beowulf then sailed back to Geatland, where he eventually became king. Many years later, when Beowulf was an old man, he died while battling a fire-breathing dragon who threatened his people.

21. Which part of the epic of Beowulf involves a quest?

    A. Beowulf's skill and strength in battle

    B. Beowolf's trip to Denmark to help the Danes

    C. Beowulf's eventually becoming king

    D. Beowulf's battle with the fire-breathing dragon

22. In which of the following ways is Beowulf typical of an epic hero?

    A. He is a high-born hero who becomes a king.

    B. He is an ordinary, everyday person.

    C. He is a talented swimmer and sailor.

    D. He is the son of a god and goddess.

23. Based on the selection, what can you conclude about the culture that produced it?

    A. It was a land-bound culture with little knowledge of the sea and sailing.

    B. It was a culture that admired courage and strength in battle.

    C. It was a culture that saw the nearby Danes as enemies.

    D. It was a culture that did not have the respect for motherhood that we have today.

Vocabulary

24. What is the term for the strict, literal meaning of a word?

    A. its denotation

    B. its connotation

    C. its annotation

    D. its association

25. Which of the following words is the most negative connotation of *odor*?
   A. fragrance
   B. smell
   C. stink
   D. scent

26. Which of the following words will best complete the sentence positively?

   Her _____ hung in the Jacksonville Museum of Modern Art.

   A. painting
   B. masterpiece
   C. artwork
   D. scribble

27. Which of the following words will best complete the sentence negatively?

   It is fine to lose weight, but do not get too _____.

   A. slender
   B. slim
   C. thin
   D. skinny

Grammar

28. Which sentence below is punctuated correctly?
   A. In the office were: an old metal desk, a large swivel chair, a new computer, and a filing cabinet.
   B. The secretary sent in an order for: pens, pencils, printer ribbons, and reams of papers.
   C. Supply the following information, your name, your address, and your phone number.
   D. Office hours are at these times: Mondays at two, Wednesdays at three, and Fridays at one.

29. Which sentence below is punctuated correctly?
   A. This year we flew to Albuquerque; we then drove from there to Santa Fe.
   B. We also visited Las Vegas, New Mexico, it is nothing like Las Vegas, Nevada.
   C. The trip lasted seven days we spent two days with Aunt Mia in Taos.
   D. We have also visited Dodge City, Kansas, Denver, Colorado, and Salt Lake City, Utah.

30. Where should you add a comma in this sentence?

   Alicia Carlos and Gabriel rehearsed for weeks and gave fine performances.

   A. after *Alicia, Carlos,* and *Gabriel*
   B. after *Alicia* and *Carlos* only
   C. after *Alicia* and *Gabriel* only
   D. after *Alicia, Carlos,* and *weeks*

31. Which sentence below is punctuated correctly?
   A. The new movie theater opens at noon, and closes at midnight on weekends.
   B. It is a modern, air-conditioned, building with four different theaters.
   C. My sister Anita, mistakenly went to the theater at noon on a Wednesday.
   D. The theater opens at five but still closes at midnight on weekdays.

32. Where should you use a colon in a business letter?
   A. after the heading
   B. after the inside address
   C. after the greeting
   D. after the closing

33. Which of the following choices is an appropriate closing for a business letter?

    A. *To Whom It May Concern* followed by a colon

    B. *Dear Madam* followed by a comma

    C. *Sincerely* followed by a colon

    D. *Respectfully* followed by a comma

ESSAY

Writing

34. Imagine that you lived long ago and had little understanding of science. Create a myth to explain one of nature's mysteries. On a separate sheet of paper, jot down your ideas for a myth explaining why the sky is blue on a sunny day or why it gets dark at night.

35. Legends often are set in distant times and unusual places. On a separate sheet of paper, write a description of a place you have encountered in a legend or a place in which you might set a legend of your own creation.

36. Imagine that you have ordered an item online or over the phone and, when it arrived, there was something wrong with it. You are now writing a business letter to complain to the company that sent the item. The company is Bruffduff & Son, 2100 Michigan Avenue, Chicago, IL 60601. Write your business letter on a separate sheet of paper. Be sure to use proper business-letter form.

Unit 6: Themes in Oral Tradition
Part 2 Concept Map

Literary Analysis:
Oral Tradition

Reading Skills and Strategies:
Comparison and Contrast

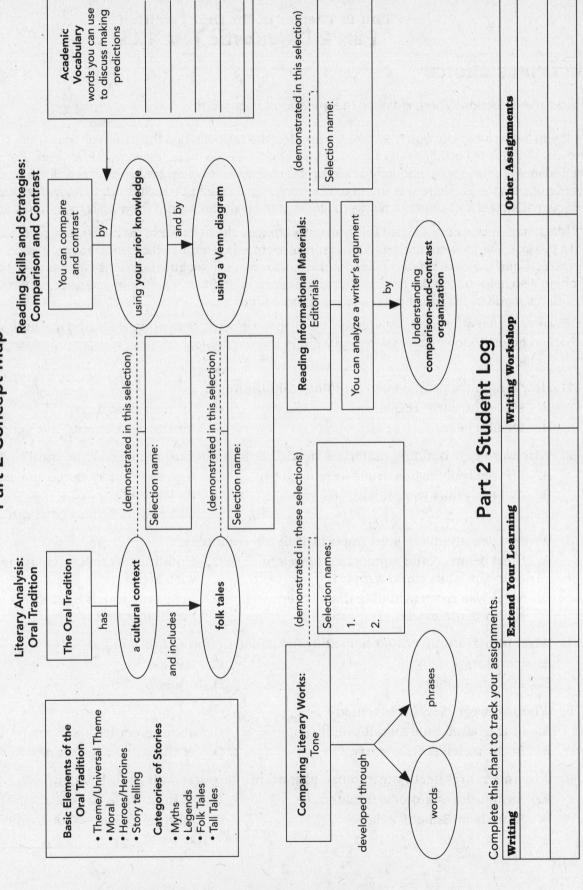

The Oral Tradition

has → **a cultural context**

and includes → **folk tales**

(demonstrated in this selection)
Selection name:

(demonstrated in this selection)
Selection name:

You can compare and contrast

by → **using your prior knowledge**

and by → **using a Venn diagram**

Academic Vocabulary
words you can use to discuss making predictions

Basic Elements of the Oral Tradition
• Theme/Universal Theme
• Moral
• Heroes/Heroines
• Story telling

Categories of Stories
• Myths
• Legends
• Folk Tales
• Tall Tales

Comparing Literary Works:
Tone

developed through → **phrases**

→ **words**

(demonstrated in these selections)
Selection names:
1.
2.

Reading Informational Materials:
Editorials

You can analyze a writer's argument

by → Understanding **comparison-and-contrast organization**

(demonstrated in this selection)
Selection name:

Part 2 Student Log

Complete this chart to track your assignments.

Writing	Extend Your Learning	Writing Workshop	Other Assignments

Unit 6: Themes in the Oral Tradition
Part 2 Diagnostic Test 12

MULTIPLE CHOICE

Read the selection. Then, answer the questions that follow.

If you live in a big city, you may take for granted the tall buildings that rise high above the city streets. However, these tall buildings have been in use for only a little more than a hundred years. Before that, materials were not strong enough to hold up tall structures. In older buildings, the walls carried the weight of the upper stories. There was a limit to how many floors could be built. With the new materials such as ready-made steel and concrete blocks, builders could shift the weight from walls to columns and beams.

Machines, such as cranes, had to be invented that could lift these huge blocks and pieces of steel high into the sky. The elevator car was a nineteenth-century invention, which became more important when architects and builders created taller buildings. Advances in electricity, plumbing, heating, and air conditioning also helped to make taller buildings possible. In addition, aluminum and glass on the sides of new buildings made outer walls lighter and let in more light.

Even with all the advances in high-rise buildings, some critics say that ideas and methods in the construction industry do not change very quickly. In this twenty-first century, you can judge for yourself.

1. How long have people been building tall buildings?
   A. since the early 1800s
   B. for fifty years
   C. for over a century
   D. for the past twenty-five years

2. Why were new building materials needed before tall buildings could be built?
   A. The old building materials were used up.
   B. Old materials were not strong enough.
   C. New machinery could not handle old materials.
   D. Old materials had gone out of fashion.

3. Why was ready-made steel important in tall buildings?
   A. Steel beams could support more weight than the walls could support.
   B. Steel was more available than other building materials.
   C. Buildings were less costly to construct with steel.
   D. Steel was much lighter than other building materials.

4. What important invention helped in the construction of tall buildings?
   A. elevators
   B. air conditioners
   C. trucks
   D. cranes

5. When was the elevator invented?
   A. at the same time as tall buildings
   B. in the nineteenth century
   C. about a century ago
   D. at the same time cranes were invented

6. Why might architects want to use aluminum for outer walls of tall buildings?
   A. Aluminum is a modern material.
   B. Aluminum is light weight.
   C. Aluminum is the cheapest material.
   D. Aluminum lasts a long time.

7. What is one criticism about the methods in the construction industry?

    A. The methods of construction have become too expensive.

    B. The methods in construction have not changed since the nineteenth century.

    C. The methods of the construction industry are too far ahead of the time.

    D. The construction industry is slow to use new ideas and methods.

Read the selection. Then, answer the questions that follow.

On April 11, 1970, Apollo 13 headed to the moon. It would be the third manned moon landing of the United States' space program. Two days into the mission, an oxygen tank exploded, and a second tank was damaged. A whole section of the service module, one of three sections of their spacecraft, collapsed.

The three astronauts' situation was serious. Luckily, the command module, which they occupied, was unharmed. Now it was not a question of completing the mission, but whether they had enough power to get home.

Scientists at NASA, the United States space agency, looked for ways to bring the astronauts safely to Earth. Finally, NASA engineers found a way to use a control system in the lunar module, which was in one piece, to remove dangerous carbon dioxide gas from the astronauts' cabin. The module's engine helped steer them home.

When the astronauts safely splashed down in the Pacific Ocean, NASA headquarters broadcast the news over television to the waiting world. In spite of the danger, everything had turned out all right.

Many people think Apollo 13 was a failure. Still, the astronauts were rescued more than 200,000 miles from Earth. From that point of view, the mission was a great success!

8. What was the mission of Apollo 13?

    A. to test the service modules

    B. to land on the moon

    C. to test NASA's spacecraft

    D. to orbit the moon

9. What dangerous accident occurred on the mission?

    A. a service module broke away

    B. the spacecraft collapsed

    C. all power to the engines was lost

    D. an oxygen tank exploded

10. What was the main problem facing the astronauts?

    A. how to complete their mission

    B. how to get home

    C. how to get more oxygen

    D. how to repair the damaged module

11. What was one important advantage the astronauts had, in spite of their trouble?

    A. The command module was not damaged.

    B. They had each other.

    C. They had plenty of power.

    D. Their mission had been completed.

12. What was the greatest danger to the astronauts?

    A. the bitter cold of space

    B. the deadly carbon dioxide gas in the cabin

    C. the inability to communicate with Earth

    D. the shortage of food

13. What piece of equipment did NASA engineers use to try to save the astronauts?

   A. a section of the spacecraft   **C.** the lunar module

   B. the command module   **D.** the oxygen tanks

14. What finally happened to the Apollo 13 mission?

   A. The mission was completed, and the astronauts returned safely to Earth.

   B. The spacecraft was recovered, but the astronauts did not survive.

   C. The mission was not completed, but the astronauts returned safely.

   D. The spacecraft crash landed, and all three astronauts were lost.

15. Why might the Apollo 13 mission be considered a success?

   A. The spacecraft was repaired, and the astronauts completed the mission as planned.

   B. The mission was not completed, but the astronauts were rescued from space.

   C. The astronauts completed their mission, even though they did not survive.

   D. The mission was completed, and the astronauts returned.

Vocabulary Warm-up Word Lists

Study these words from "Sun and Moon in a Box." Then, complete the activities that follow.

Word List A

burden [BER den] *n.* a load that is carried
Barbara found carrying the suitcase to be a <u>burden</u>.

cunning [KUHN ing] *adj.* clever, sly
The <u>cunning</u> thief knew how to avoid being caught.

eagle [EE guhl] *n.* a large bird of the hawk family
The <u>eagle</u> built its nest high on a cliff.

lag [LAG] *v.* to fall behind
Roger will <u>lag</u> behind in the race if he does not practice.

relented [ri LENT ed] *v.* became less stubborn or set in one's ways
Mary's sister <u>relented</u> and allowed Mary to borrow her earrings.

reliable [ri LYE uh buhl] *adj.* dependable or trustworthy
The <u>reliable</u> clock kept very good time.

talons [TAL uhnz] *n.* sharp claws
The hawk's sharp <u>talons</u> clutched its prey.

wooded [WOOD id] *adj.* covered with woods or trees
The cottage was located in a heavily <u>wooded</u> area.

Word List B

betray [bee TRAY] *v.* to break faith or trust
Paul told Ben that he would not <u>betray</u> Ben's trust.

embarrassed [em BAR uhst] *v.* caused to feel self-conscious
The praise she received <u>embarrassed</u> her and made her blush.

grasshoppers [GRAS hahp erz] *n.* leaping, plant-eating insects with powerful hind legs
The <u>grasshoppers</u> jumped a long distance in the garden.

objected [uhb JEKT ed] *v.* opposed
Sally's father <u>objected</u> to the late hour she said she would return home.

outer [OWT er] *adj.* located farther out than another spot or place
You must peel the <u>outer</u> part of an orange before eating it.

pestering [PES ter ing] *v.* bothering or annoying endlessly
The puppy would not stop <u>pestering</u> Amy for a treat.

regretted [ri GRET id] *v.* felt sorry about something that happened
Tom <u>regretted</u> that he did not have a chance to say good-bye to his friend.

rely [ri LY] *v.* to count on, to depend
Can I <u>rely</u> on you to pick me up at the train station tonight?

Name _____ Date _____

Vocabulary Warm-up Exercises

Exercise A *Fill in each blank in the paragraph below with an appropriate word from Word List A. Use each word only once.*

Mike wanted to be a(n) [1] _____ for the costume ball. He loved these

powerful, [2] _____ birds of prey. At first, Mike's mom said no, because

she didn't know how she'd make such a costume. At last, however, good, old

[3] _____ Mom [4] _____ and said yes. She made him a

great costume complete with giant feathers and big [5] _____ to wear as

claws on his feet. On the night of the ball, Mike had a great time swooping around his

[6] _____ yard, as he pretended to fly. The only problem was dancing at

the ball. Then the feathers and claws became a heavy [7] _____ to move

around in. Mike began to [8] _____ behind the others in the conga line.

Once he took them off, however, he felt as light as a feather!

Exercise B *Revise each sentence so that the underlined vocabulary word is used in a logical way. Be sure to keep the vocabulary word in your revision.*

Example: After Barry became <u>embarrassed</u>, he felt very confident.
After Barry became <u>embarrassed</u>, he felt very self-conscious.

1. The <u>grasshoppers</u> could not jump very far with their powerful hind legs.
   _____

2. If we lie and <u>betray</u> our friends, they will learn they can <u>rely</u> on us.
   _____

3. It is very pleasant when someone is continuously <u>pestering</u> us.
   _____

4. The <u>outer</u> layer of clothing is the hardest one to remove if you are too warm.
   _____

5. The majority of voters <u>objected</u> to the proposed law, so it easily passed.
   _____

6. Because Tom <u>regretted</u> his rudeness, he decided not to apologize.
   _____

Name _____ Date _____

"Sun and Moon in a Box" by Richard Erdoes and Alfonso Ortiz
Reading Warm-up A

Read the following passage. Pay special attention to the underlined words. Then, read it again, and complete the activities. Use a separate sheet of paper for your written answers.

July 21

Dear Cousin Wayne,

I'm writing to you from the great nature camp I'm attending this summer! As you know, I love learning about animals, so Mom and Dad finally <u>relented</u>, after a lot of pleading on my part. They are letting me spend the summer here.

The camp is located in a <u>wooded</u> area. It is near the cliffs that overlook the river. It is an excellent spot for observing an <u>eagle</u> that lives atop the cliffs. Every day, I study the habits of this powerful bird. Like its cousin, the hawk, the eagle is a <u>cunning</u> predator. It hunts rabbits, mice, and other birds. Those are just a few of the animals it likes to eat.

I have watched the eagle as it circles a flock of mourning doves that eat on the ground near our cabin. As they realize that the eagle is descending upon them, most of the doves take flight. Often, though, one of them may <u>lag</u> behind. The eagle will swoop at the slower bird. Often the dove becomes flustered and might hit against one of the windows of the cabin. The eagle quickly grasps the prey in its sharp <u>talons</u> and flies away with it. It all seems to happen in one smooth motion.

The eagle's wingspan is wide. It beats its wings powerfully as it flies away. The prey it carries in its claws is not a heavy <u>burden</u> for it.

Although I have not seen if this eagle has hatched any chicks yet, I am going to continue to watch its nest. I have read that eagles are devoted, <u>reliable</u> parents, who always bring food back to the nest for the hungry chicks.

So far, this has been a great summer! Please write back soon and let me know what you are up to.

Love, your cousin,

Ben

1. Circle the words that tell what Ben did so that his parents <u>relented</u>. Define *relented.*

2. Underline the words that tell what is located in a <u>wooded</u> area in the story. What else might be found in a *wooded* area?

3. Circle the words that describe where the <u>eagle</u> lives. What is an *eagle*?

4. Underline the word that <u>cunning</u> describes. What is a synonym for *cunning*?

5. Underline two sentences that tell what the eagle does if a bird happens to <u>lag</u> behind. Use *lag* in a sentence.

6. Circle the words that tell what the eagle grasps in its <u>talons</u>. What other animals have *talons*?

7. Circle the words that tell what is not a heavy <u>burden</u> for the eagle. Define *burden.*

8. Underline the words that tell why eagles are <u>reliable</u> parents. Use *reliable* in a sentence.

Name _____ Date _____

"Sun and Moon in a Box" by Richard Erdoes and Alfonso Ortiz
Reading Warm-up B

Read the following passage. Pay special attention to the underlined words. Then, read it again, and complete the activities. Use a separate sheet of paper for your written answers.

The Zuni are a Native American people who live in what is now the southwest United States. Together with the Hopi and Acoma peoples of this desert region, the Zuni are known as Pueblos.

The apartment-like structures the Zunis traditionally lived in are known as pueblo dwellings. These were made of stone and logs and had many levels. The <u>outer</u> rooms housed the families. These apartments surrounded a central courtyard. The families were used to living together, so they were not <u>embarrassed</u> by living in such close quarters.

When Spanish soldiers invaded the area for the second time in the 1680s, the Zuni people were wary of them. The natives feared that the invaders would <u>betray</u> the Zunis' trust. The tribe decided it was safer to move to a high, flat area, away from the soldiers.

The Zunis grew crops in the desert. The men hunted, made tools, and created jewelry. The women gathered and grew the food, cared for the children, and made pottery and baskets. Both men and women built and took care of the houses. If children wanted to join in the work, no one <u>objected</u>. The children's questions were not seen as <u>pestering</u> the adults. The children were welcomed, for that was how the Zunis could <u>rely</u> on being able to pass traditional skills on to the younger generation.

During the years, unfortunately, some traditional skills and cultural activities faded away, as European practices took their place. Many Zuni people <u>regretted</u> this state of affairs. They have since worked very hard to revive their native culture. Jewelry, pottery, and sculptures are some of the art forms created by the Zuni. The sculptures are carved from stones and minerals and represent <u>grasshoppers</u>, bears, skunks, and other animals.

Traditional beliefs, dances, and rituals are also practiced by some of today's Zuni, as they strive to keep their culture alive.

1. Underline the words that tell how the <u>outer</u> rooms of the pueblo were used. Define *outer*.

2. Circle the words that tell why the people were not <u>embarrassed</u>. What is a synonym for *embarrassed*?

3. Circle the word that tells who the Zunis thought might <u>betray</u> them. Use *betray* in a sentence.

4. Underline the words that tell to what situation no one <u>objected</u>. To what have you ever *objected*?

5. Underline the words that tell what the adults did not view as <u>pestering</u> them. What is a synonym for *pestering*?

6. Circle the words that tell upon what the Zunis could <u>rely</u>. Use *rely* in a sentence.

7. Underline the sentence that explains the state of affairs that the Zunis <u>regretted</u>. What have you ever *regretted*?

8. Underline the words that tell from what the sculptures of <u>grasshoppers</u> are made. What are *grasshoppers*?

"Sun and Moon in a Box" by Richard Erdoes and Alfonso Ortiz

Reading: Use Prior Knowledge to Compare and Contrast

A **comparison** tells how two or more things are alike. A **contrast** tells how two or more things are different. When you **compare and contrast,** you recognize similarities and differences. You can often understand an unfamiliar concept by **using your prior knowledge to compare and contrast.** For example, you may understand an ancient culture better if you look for ways in which it is similar to and different from your own culture. You also might find similarities and differences between a story told long ago and one that is popular today. To compare and contrast stories, ask questions such as "What does this event bring to mind?" or "Does this character make me think of someone I know or have read about?"

DIRECTIONS: *Read each passage from "Sun and Moon in a Box." In the second column of the chart, write a question that will help you compare or contrast the passage to something else you have read or to something or someone you know or know about. In the third column, write the answer to your question. The first item has been completed as an example.*

Passage from "Sun and Moon in a Box"	Question Based on My Prior Knowledge	Comparison or Contrast
1. Coyote and Eagle were hunting. Eagle caught rabbits. Coyote caught nothing but grasshoppers. Coyote said, "Friend Eagle, my chief, we make a great hunting pair."	How are these characters like Wile E. Coyote and Road Runner in the cartoons I used to watch?	Road Runner is a bird, but not an eagle, and Wile E. Coyote tries to catch him. Here, the coyote and the eagle seem to be friends.
2. Whenever [the Kachinas] wanted light they opened the lid and let the sun peek out. Then, it was day. When they wanted less light, they opened the box just a little for the moon to look out.		
3. After a while Coyote called Eagle, "My chief, let me have the box. I am ashamed to let you do all the carrying." "No," said Eagle, "You are not reliable. You might be curious and open the box."		
4. [Coyote] sat down and opened the box. In a flash, . . . icy winds made all living things shiver. Then, before Coyote could put the lid back, . . . snow fell down from heaven and covered the plains and the mountains.		

Name _____ Date _____

Literary Analysis: Cultural Context

Stories such as fables, folk tales, and myths are influenced by cultural context. **Cultural context** is the background, customs, and beliefs of the people who originally told them. Knowing the cultural context of a work will help you understand and appreciate it. You can keep track of the cultural context of a work by considering these elements: the *title* of the selection, the *time* in which it takes place, the *place* in which it takes place, the *customs* of the characters, the *beliefs* that are expressed or suggested.

Consider this passage from "Sun and Moon in a Box":

Now, at this time, the earth was still soft and new. There was as yet no sun and no moon.

The passage tells you that the folk tale is set in the distant past, before Earth looked as it does today and before there was a sun and a moon. From the cultural context, you can infer that the people who told the tale believed there was a time when Earth existed, but the sun and the moon as yet did not.

DIRECTIONS: *Read each passage from "Sun and Moon in a Box." In the second column of the chart, indicate which element of the cultural context—time, place, customs, or beliefs—the passage illustrates. Then, explain your choice. Tell why you think the example shows the element you have chosen.*

Passage from "Sun and Moon in a Box"	Element of Cultural Context and Explanation
1. [Eagle and Coyote] went toward the west. They came to a deep canyon.	
2. Whenever [the Kachinas] wanted light they opened the lid and let the sun peek out. . . . When they wanted less light, they opened the box just a little for the moon to look out.	
3. "Let us steal the box," said Coyote. "No, that would be wrong," said Eagle. "Let us just borrow it."	
4. Eagle grabbed the box and . . . Coyote ran after him on the ground. After a while Coyote called Eagle: "My chief, let me have the box. I am ashamed to let you do all the carrying."	

Name _____ Date _____

"Sun and Moon in a Box" by Richard Erdoes and Alfonso Ortiz
Vocabulary Builder

Word List

```
reliable        relented        curb
```

A. DIRECTIONS: *For each item below, think about the meaning of the underlined word from the Word List. Then, answer the question and explain your answer.*

1. Zach lent a book to his most <u>reliable</u> classmate, Tyler. Was Tyler likely to return the book?

   _____

   _____

2. For days, the children pleaded with their parents to let them keep the stray dog, and, at last, their parents <u>relented</u>. Did the family keep the dog?

   _____

   _____

3. As summer vacation approached and Ashley looked forward to going away, she could not stop herself from making lists and plans. Was she able to <u>curb</u> her excitement?

   _____

   _____

B. DIRECTIONS: *Indicate whether each statement is* true *or* false. *Then, explain your answer.*

1. A car that starts only half the time is *reliable.*

   T / F: _____ **Explanation:** _____

   _____

2. A teacher who refuses her students' pleas to make a test easier has *relented.*

   T / F: _____ **Explanation:** _____

   _____

3. Someone who can keep a secret is able to *curb* the desire to tell his or her best friend everything.

   T / F: _____ **Explanation:** _____

   _____

Name _____ Date _____

"Sun and Moon in a Box" by Richard Erdoes and Alfonso Ortiz
Support for Writing a Plot Summary

Use this chart to take notes for a **plot summary** of "Sun and Moon in a Box."

Plot Summary of "Sun and Moon in a Box"

Setting:	
Major character Eagle:	**Major character Coyote:**

Main event from beginning of folk tale:	Main event from middle of folk tale:	Main event from end of folk tale:

Final outcome:

Now, use your notes to write your **plot summary.** Be sure to include all the information called for on the chart.

"Sun and Moon in a Box" by Richard Erdoes and Alfonso Ortiz
Support for Extend Your Learning

Research and Technology

Use the following chart to take notes for the **feature article** you will write about Zuni culture. Use the topics suggested here, or focus on topics of your own choosing. Look for a fact or detail that will grab your readers' attention. Look for phrases you can use as headings to emphasize main ideas. Finally, be sure every paragraph you write has a main idea and supporting details.

Who Are the Zuni? Where Did They Live?	How Was Traditional Zuni Society Structured? How Did the Zuni Live?	What Are Some Traditional Zuni Beliefs and Customs?

Listening and Speaking

Use the following prompts as you work with a partner to gather unusual facts about an animal in preparation for a **story** you will make up and present to your classmates. Remember: You will not name the animal in your presentation.

Unusual fact 1: _____

Unusual fact 2: _____

Unusual fact 3: _____

Unusual fact 4: _____

Unusual fact 5: _____

Facial expressions, gestures, and movements that identify the animal: _____

_____

Dialogue: _____

_____

_____

_____

Name _____ Date _____

"Sun and Moon in a Box" by Richard Erdoes and Alfonso Ortiz
Enrichment: Coyote, the Character With Many Roles

"Sun and Moon in a Box" is not the only story in which Coyote plays a part. Coyote characters are extremely common in Native American tales and myths. In those stories, Coyote plays many roles.

Sometimes, Coyote is a hero. Then, he is part human, or he helps humans. In one tale, Coyote helps defeat a monster that is eating all the other animals.

At other times, Coyote is a trickster. As a trickster, Coyote fools humans and other animals. As a trickster, Coyote likes to steal things and make trouble. The key to the trickster character is survival. Whatever people or other animals do to him, Coyote survives and comes out on top. As a trickster, Coyote is somewhat like the real-life coyote of today. Many ranchers do not like coyotes because they prey on the ranchers' livestock. Consider the situation from the coyote's point of view, however: The animal is only trying to survive.

Coyote can also play the fool. Like any fool, Coyote lacks judgment. He does stupid things.

No matter what his role, the Coyote of myth and folklore often teaches a moral lesson.

Directions: *Answer the following questions. Support your responses with evidence from the preceding passage, your reading of "Sun and Moon in a Box," and anything else you know about the role of Coyote in folklore.*

1. Does Coyote play the role of a hero in "Sun and Moon in a Box"? How can you tell?

    _____

    _____

2. Does Coyote play the role of a trickster and/or a survivor in "Sun and Moon in a Box"? How can you tell?

    _____

    _____

    _____

    _____

3. Does Coyote play the role of a fool in "Sun and Moon in a Box"? How can you tell?

    _____

    _____

4. Does Coyote teach a moral lesson in "Sun and Moon in a Box"? Defend your answer. If he does teach a lesson, explain what it is.

    _____

    _____

    _____

"Sun and Moon in a Box" by Richard Erdoes and Alfonso Ortiz
Selection Test A

Critical Reading *Identify the letter of the choice that best answers the question.*

_____ 1. Where does "Sun and Moon in a Box" take place?
   A. in the West
   B. in a city
   C. in outer space
   D. on a mountaintop

_____ 2. Who are the main characters in "Sun and Moon in a Box"?
   A. the Kachinas
   B. the Sun and the Moon
   C. Eagle and Coyote
   D. summer and winter

_____ 3. In "Sun and Moon in a Box," the narrator says,
   Eagle regretted to have Coyote for a companion.

   Why does he say that?
   A. Eagle realizes that Coyote is a thief.
   B. Eagle has to do all the hunting to feed the two of them.
   C. Eagle must carry Coyote across the canyons and rivers.
   D. Eagle does not want to share the sun and the moon with Coyote.

_____ 4. According to "Sun and Moon in a Box," for what do the Kachinas use the sun and the moon?
   A. to create the seasons
   B. to create day and night
   C. to light their homes
   D. to light their dances

_____ 5. In "Sun and Moon in a Box," how are Eagle and Coyote alike?
   A. They are Kachina dancers.
   B. They want to steal the box.
   C. They are creatures who hunt.
   D. They are humans in disguise.

_____ 6. In "Sun and Moon in a Box," which statements describe ways in which Coyote and Eagle are different?

      I.   Eagle can fly, and Coyote can run.

      II. Eagle catches rabbits, and Coyote catches grasshoppers.

      III. Eagle can talk, but Coyote cannot talk.

      IV. Eagle wants to borrow the box, and Coyote wants to steal it.

      A. I, II, III   **B.** II, II, IV   **C.** I, II, IV   **D.** I, III, IV

_____ 7. In "Sun and Moon in a Box," Eagle is afraid to let Coyote carry the box. What trait of Coyote's is he worried about?

      A. his intelligence

      B. his laziness

      C. his dishonesty

      D. his pride

_____ 8. In "Sun and Moon in a Box," what is Coyote's real reason for asking Eagle to let him carry the box?

      A. He wants it for himself.

      B. He wants to share the work.

      C. He wants to return it.

      D. He wants to let the sun escape.

_____ 9. In "Sun and Moon in a Box," what happens when Coyote opens the box?

      A. The sun blinds him forever.

      B. He grows a winter coat for warmth.

      C. The sun and moon escape, and winter comes.

      D. Eagle captures the sun and moon and returns them to the box.

_____ 10. According to "Sun and Moon in a Box," what is the climate like before Coyote opens the box?

      A. It is summer all the time.

      B. There are two seasons, spring and fall.

      C. There are two seasons, summer and winter.

      D. There are four seasons.

_____ 11. Which word best describes Eagle's action in giving the box to Coyote?

      A. mean

      B. cautious

      C. foolish

      D. helpful

_____ 12. Based on your reading of "Sun and Moon in a Box," you can draw conclusions about the beliefs of the Zuni people, the tellers of this story. Which statements best describe their beliefs?

    I. The sun and the moon are precious.

    II. The box should be hidden in a canyon.

    III. It is important to keep one's promises.

    IV. The eagle is trustworthy; the coyote is not.

    A. I, II, III   **B.** I, III, IV   **C.** II, III, IV   **D.** I, II, IV

_____ 13. What kind of work is "Sun and Moon in a Box"?

    A. a drama

    B. a folk tale

    C. a biography

    D. an essay

Vocabulary and Grammar

_____ 14. In which sentence is the meaning of the word *relented* expressed?

    A. Coyote begged and begged Eagle to let him carry the box.

    B. The Kachinas kept the sun and the moon in a box and used them wisely.

    C. Eagle at last gave in to Coyote and allowed him to carry the box.

    D. The sun and the moon flew into the sky, causing a change in the climate.

_____ 15. In which sentence is the capitalization correct?

    A. "My chief, I cannot fly," said coyote.

    B. "Let us steal the box," said coyote.

    C. "No, I don't trust you," Eagle repeated.

    D. "my chief, I am really embarrassed."

Essay

16. Several times Coyote asks Eagle to let him carry the box, and each time Eagle says no. At last, Eagle takes pity on Coyote and lets him carry it. As you were reading "Sun and Moon in a Box," did you think that Eagle should have let Coyote carry the box? Why or why not? Explain your response in an essay. Cite a detail from the story to support your point of view.

17. In what ways are Coyote and Eagle alike? In what ways are they different? In an essay, cite at least one example from "Sun and Moon in a Box" that shows the two characters' similarities and at least one example that shows their differences.

Name _____ Date _____

"Sun and Moon in a Box" by Richard Erdoes and Alfonso Ortiz
Selection Test B

Critical Reading *Identify the letter of the choice that best completes the statement or answers the question.*

____ 1. What is the setting of the opening of "Sun and Moon in a Box"?
   A. the present day
   B. the distant future
   C. a time before animals roamed the earth
   D. a time before the sun and the moon were in the sky

____ 2. In "Sun and Moon in a Box," what are the Kachinas doing when Coyote and Eagle first see them?
   A. eating
   B. hunting
   C. dancing
   D. singing

____ 3. According to "Sun and Moon in a Box," for what do the Kachinas use the sun and the moon?
   A. to create day and night
   B. to heat their pueblo
   C. to search out prey to hunt
   D. to create the seasons

____ 4. Based on "Sun and Moon in a Box", what can you infer about the Kachinas?
   A. They keep all pretty things for themselves.
   B. They treat the sun and the moon as if they were precious.
   C. They keep every element of nature in a box.
   D. They want to attract the attention of Eagle and Coyote.

____ 5. The following statements are based on contrasts between Eagle and Coyote in "Sun and Moon in a Box." Which statement most likely reflects a traditional belief of the Zuni?
   A. Rabbits are superior to grasshoppers.
   B. Flying is more highly valued than running.
   C. Flying is more highly valued than swimming.
   D. Borrowing is acceptable, but stealing is not.

____ 6. In "Sun and Moon in a Box," why does Eagle say that the box is "precious"?
   A. It is covered with jewels.
   B. It is made of gold.
   C. It contains the sun and the moon.
   D. It belongs to the Kachinas.

____ 7. Which of the following statements best summarizes the argument Coyote makes to persuade Eagle to let him carry the box?
A. Others will think badly of me if I let you do all the work.
B. I will share the blame with you when the Kachinas find us.
C. You took the box originally, so I should be the one to carry it.
D. I always keep my promises, so let me carry the box.

____ 8. In "Sun and Moon in a Box," why does Eagle allow Coyote to carry the box?
A. He is tired of carrying it.
B. He wants to trust Coyote.
C. He regrets having taken it.
D. He is playing a trick on Coyote.

____ 9. Toward the end of "Sun and Moon in a Box," Eagle says,

"I knew what kind of low, cunning, stupid creature you are. I should have remembered that you never keep a promise."

What can you infer from Eagle's remark?
A. Coyote and Eagle have just met.
B. Eagle has a good memory.
C. Eagle is more intelligent than Coyote.
D. Coyote has broken promises before.

____ 10. How does the setting at the beginning of "Sun and Moon in a Box" compare with the setting at the end?
A. The beginning takes place in a canyon, and the end takes place at a river.
B. The beginning takes place in summer, and the end takes place in winter.
C. The beginning takes place in the sky, and the end takes place on the ground.
D. The beginning takes place by a river, and the end takes place at Kachina Pueblo.

____ 11. Which statement describes a similarity between Eagle and Coyote in "Sun and Moon in a Box"?
A. Both are trustworthy.
B. Both are swimmers.
C. Both are hunters.
D. Both are cunning.

____ 12. Which statement describes a belief of the Zuni that is expressed in "Sun and Moon in a Box"?
A. Animals are more powerful than humans.
B. Animals are deceitful and cunning.
C. Animals have character traits.
D. Animals are trustworthy and strong.

____ 13. Based on "Sun and Moon in a Box," you can infer that the Zuni traditionally believed coyotes are
A. stupid.
B. dishonest.
C. poor hunters.
D. excellent hunters.

___ 14. Based on "Sun and Moon in a Box," you can infer that the Zuni traditionally valued
   A. cunning.
   B. curiosity.
   C. reliability.
   D. beauty.

Vocabulary and Grammar

___ 15. In which sentence is the word *relented* used correctly?
   A. Eagle *relented* and let Coyote carry the box.
   B. Coyote *relented* and refused to say he was sorry.
   C. Eagle *relented* and did not change his position.
   D. Coyote *relented* and kept making the same point.

___ 16. In which sentence is the meaning of the word *curb* expressed?
   A. The Kachinas protected the sun and the moon.
   B. Eagle flew over the canyons, far above Coyote.
   C. Coyote was unable to control his curiosity.
   D. The sun and the moon escaped from the box.

___ 17. In which sentence is the capitalization correct?
   A. Coyote said to Eagle, "you see, I cannot fly."
   B. Coyote said to eagle, "you see, I cannot fly."
   C. Coyote said to eagle, "You see, I cannot fly."
   D. Coyote said to Eagle, "You see, I cannot fly."

___ 18. In which sentence is the capitalization correct?
   A. "No, I won't give you the box," Said eagle to coyote.
   B. "No, i won't give you the box," said eagle to coyote.
   C. "No, I won't give you the box," said Eagle to Coyote.
   D. "No, I won't give you the box," Said Eagle to Coyote.

Essay

19. In your opinion, is Eagle fully responsible for the appearance of the first winter in "Sun and Moon in a Box"? Is he partly responsible? Does he bear no responsibility at all? Why or why not? In an essay, give your opinion. Cite at least two details from the selection to support your position.

20. Many cultures have traditionally used stories with animal characters to comment on human behavior. What comments about human behavior might the Zuni be making in "Sun and Moon in a Box"? In an essay, describe Coyote and Eagle as they are portrayed in the selection. Then, tell what message about human behavior the selection makes.

Vocabulary Warm-up Word Lists

Study these words from "How the Snake Got Poison." Then, complete the activities that follow.

Word List A

belly [BEL ee] *n.* the stomach or underside of an animal
   The puppy's <u>belly</u> was round and full after it ate.

claws [KLAWZ] *n.* an animal's sharp, curved nails
   The cat used its <u>claws</u> for digging, scratching, and climbing.

enemy [EN uh mee] *n.* someone who wishes to hurt another
   The soldiers were trained to combat the <u>enemy</u> during battle.

fight [FYT] *v.* to take part in a physical struggle or battle
   The two boxers will <u>fight</u> in the boxing ring.

poison [POY zuhn] *n.* a substance that causes death or illness
   The skull-and-crossbones label on the paint meant it was <u>poison</u>.

rattles [RAT uhlz] *n.* rings on a rattlesnake's tail that make a rattling sound
   The hikers thought they heard the warning sound of <u>rattles</u> nearby.

shakes [SHAYKS] *v.* causes to move up and down or sideways
   The ground <u>shakes</u> with every step the giant takes.

snakes [SNAYKS] *n.* long, scaly reptiles without legs or feet
   At the zoo, the <u>snakes</u> slid across the floor of their cage.

Word List B

earth [ERTH] *n.* the planet we live on, or this world
   Countless species of insects live on the <u>earth</u>.

generations [jen uh RAY shuhnz] *n.* the relatives who have come before or will come after someone
   To future <u>generations</u>, today's events will be history.

immensity [i MEN si tee] *n.* immeasurable largeness or vastness
   The <u>immensity</u> of space is hard to imagine.

ornament [AWR nuh muhnt] *v.* to decorate
   During the holidays, the pine boughs served to <u>ornament</u> the house.

protection [pruh TEK shuhn] *n.* a defense; something that shields one from danger
   One form of <u>protection</u> for the president is a bodyguard.

stomped [STAHMT] *v.* injured or killed by stamping on
   The farmer <u>stomped</u> on the biting ants that came out where he was digging.

subject [SUHB jekt] *n.* topic being studied or thought about
   The student council discussed the <u>subject</u> of new playground equipment.

towards [TAWRDZ] *prep.* in the direction of
   Each morning, we walked in the same direction <u>towards</u> the school.

Name _____ Date _____

"How the Snake Got Poison" by Zora Neale Hurston
Vocabulary Warm-up Exercises

Exercise A *Fill in each blank in the paragraph below with an appropriate word from Word List A. Use each word only once.*

Robby loved to watch old Westerns, the type of movie with a cowboy hero who would [1] _____ an evil [2] _____, such as a bank robber. In some movies, the cowboy had to battle dangerous creatures of nature, such as powerful bears with sharp [3] _____ or slithering [4] _____ of the kind that crawls on its [5] _____. The most dangerous of these had fangs filled with [6] _____ that could kill you with one bite. Before striking, however, Robby knew this animal [7] _____ the [8] _____ on its tail as a warning. Such movie scenes were always exciting to watch!

Exercise B *Find a synonym for each word in the following list. Then, use each synonym in a sentence that makes its meaning clear. Refer to a thesaurus if you need help finding a synonym.*

Example: towards **Synonym:** *at*
The arrow was aimed at the target.

1. immensity   **Synonym:** _____

_____

2. earth   **Synonym:** _____

_____

3. ornament   **Synonym:** _____

_____

4. protection   **Synonym:** _____

_____

5. stomped   **Synonym:** _____

_____

6. generations   **Synonym:** _____

_____

7. subject   **Synonym:** _____

_____

Name _____ Date _____

Read the following passage. Pay special attention to the underlined words. Then, read it again, and complete the activities. Use a separate sheet of paper for your written answers.

Snakes are reptiles that have no legs. A snake moves along the ground by contracting the muscles on its belly. Some snakes also use these muscles for climbing trees.

Snakes live in many places of the world. Some are born live from their mother's body. Many others are hatched from tough, leathery eggs.

Baby rattlesnakes have a special pointed egg tooth, which grows on the tip of its nose. The baby snake uses the egg tooth to poke a hole through the egg when it is ready to be hatched.

Even as babies, rattlesnakes have a deadly poison in their fangs. Because of its lethal bite, people and other animals are wary of the rattlesnake. Even such animals as mountain lions or bears, with their strong jaws and teeth and sharp, pointed claws, do not try to fight a rattlesnake.

If a rattlesnake is threatened, it first gives a warning before it strikes. It shakes the series of rings called rattles that grow on its tail. This sound means danger!

Rattlesnakes belong to a larger group of snakes called pit vipers. This kind of snake has heat-sensitive pits on either side of its head. These pits help the snake find warm-blooded prey.

Most snakes are not poisonous. They are, however, the enemy of the animals they like to eat. Such prey includes toads, lizards, mice, and birds.

The python is a snake that kills its prey by squeezing it. The unlucky animal suffocates. The snake then eats it all in one bite. Large pythons can swallow an entire pig. The snake's lower jaw unhinges, which allows its mouth to open wide.

Snakes are an interesting group of reptiles. Perhaps you will visit a zoo or visit a zoo camera site on the Internet. If so, be sure to take a firsthand look at these fascinating creatures.

1. Circle the words that tell how snakes are different from other reptiles. Name a few kinds of *snakes*.

2. Circle the words that tell why the snake contracts the muscles of its belly. Define *belly*.

3. Underline the word that describes the rattlesnake's poison. Use *poison* in a sentence.

4. Circle the words that give two examples of animals with claws. What other animals have *claws*?

5. Underline the word that tells what the mountain lions or bears try not to fight. Define *fight*.

6. Circle the words that tell what the rattlesnake shakes for a warning. Use *shakes* in a sentence.

7. Underline the words that tell where the rattles grow. What are *rattles*?

8. Underline the words that tell to which animals the snakes are an enemy. Define *enemy*.

Name _____ Date _____

Read the following passage. Pay special attention to the underlined words. Then, read it again, and complete the activities. Use a separate sheet of paper for your written answers.

There are many kinds of plants and animals on our earth. No matter how large or small, each one plays an important part in the balance of nature. The balance of nature is how our planet survives. It is the chain of events that take place between plants and animals.

For example, in the grasslands of the world, there is a partnership between the plants and animals that live there. The growing grass and the graceful antelopes may look very lovely. They serve a more serious purpose than to merely ornament the world, however. The grazing animals survive by eating the grass. They give back nutrients to the soil in their waste. That, in turn, helps more grass to grow. People also benefit from this by eating the animals that are fed by the grass.

In every habitat on the planet, partnerships take place. The immensity of the world's many habitats is an amazing subject to ponder. We need to be aware of how we affect these habitats. Unfortunately, human actions sometimes have a bad effect on the balance of nature. One example of this was the way humans hunted many kinds of whales almost to extinction. If the whales were completely wiped out, much the way a colony of termites might be stomped out by an exterminator, then future generations of whales could not exist. As a consequence, the balance of nature in the ocean would be upset. Whales would not be there to play their part.

Some people realized the negative effects of such actions. They worked towards educating others about the importance of the balance of nature. Today, scientists believe the best protection for keeping a species of animals alive is by preserving the entire habitat in which it lives. This is an important challenge to us all.

1. Underline the words that tell what there are many of on earth. Define *earth*.

2. Circle the words that tell what serves to do more than ornament the world. How would you *ornament* your room?

3. Circle the words that tell what is an immensity in the world. What is an antonym of *immensity*?

4. Underline the words that tell what is an amazing subject to ponder. What *subject* do you wonder about?

5. Underline what might be stomped out by an exterminator. What does *stomped* mean?

6. Circle the words that tell what would happen to future generations of whales. Use *generations* in a sentence.

7. Circle the words that tell what people are working towards. What are you working *towards*?

8. Underline the words that tell what scientists believe is the best protection for keeping a species alive. Use *protection* in a sentence.

Name _____ Date _____

"How the Snake Got Poison" by Zora Neale Hurston

Reading: Use Prior Knowledge to Compare and Contrast

A **comparison** tells how two or more things are alike. A **contrast** tells how two or more things are different. When you **compare and contrast,** you recognize similarities and differences. You can often understand an unfamiliar concept by **using your prior knowledge to compare and contrast.** For example, you may understand an ancient culture better if you look for ways in which it is similar to and different from your own culture. You also might find similarities and differences between a story told long ago and one that is popular today. To compare and contrast stories, ask questions such as "What does this event bring to mind?" or "Does this character make me think of someone I know or have read about?"

DIRECTIONS: *Read each passage from "How the Snake Got Poison." In the second column of the chart, write a question that will help you compare or contrast the passage to something else you have read or to something or someone you know or know about. In the third column, write the answer to your question. The first item has been completed as an example.*

Passage from "How the Snake Got Poison"	Question Based on My Prior Knowledge	Comparison or Contrast
1. "Ah ain't so many, God, you put me down here on my belly in de dust and everything trods upon me and kills off my generations. Ah ain't got no kind of protection at all."	How does this snake compare with Nag and Nagaina in the story "Rikki-tikki-tavi"?	Like this snake, Nag and Nagaina can talk. They also have a problem protecting themselves and their unborn children.
2. "God, please do somethin' 'bout dat snake. He' layin' in de bushes there wid poison in his mouf and he's strikin' everything dat shakes de bushes. He's killin' up our generations."		
3. "Lawd, you know Ah'm down here in de dust. Ah ain't got no claws to fight wid, and Ah ain't got no feets to git me out de way. All Ah kin see is feets comin' to tromple me. Ah can't tell who my enemy is. . . ."		
4. "Well, snake, I don't want yo' generations all stomped out and I don't want you killin' everything else dat moves. Here take dis bell and tie it to yo' tail."		

"How the Snake Got Poison" by Zora Neale Hurston
Literary Analysis: Cultural Context

Stories such as fables, folk tales, and myths are influenced by cultural context. **Cultural context** is the background, customs, and beliefs of the people who originally told them. Knowing the cultural context of a work will help you understand and appreciate it. You can keep track of the cultural context of a work by considering these elements: the *title* of the selection, the *time* in which it takes place, the *place* in which it takes place, the *customs* of the characters, the *beliefs* that are expressed or suggested.

Consider this passage from "How the Snake Got Poison":

Well, when God made de snake he put him in de bushes to ornament de ground.

The passage tells you that the folk tale is set in the distant past. From the cultural context, you can infer that the people who told the tale held beliefs about the purpose of the snake in nature.

DIRECTIONS: *These passages from "How the Snake Got Poison" illustrate the folk tale's cultural context by suggesting beliefs held by the people who told the tale. In the second column of the chart, tell what belief the passage illustrates.*

Passage from "How the Snake Got Poison"	Suggested Belief
1. God . . . said, "Ah didn't mean for nothin' to be stompin' you snakes lak dat. You got to have some kind of a protection. Here, take dis poison and put it in yo' mouf and when they tromps on you, protect yo'self."	
2. "Snake, . . . Ah didn't mean for you to be hittin' and killin' everything dat shake de bush. I give you dat poison and tole you to protect yo'self when they tromples on you. But you killin' everything dat moves."	
3. "Here take dis bell and tie it to yo' tail. When you hear feets comin' you ring yo' bell and if it's yo' friend, he'll be keerful. If it's yo' enemy, it's you and him."	

"How the Snake Got Poison" by Zora Neale Hurston
Vocabulary Builder

Word List

ornament	immensity

A. DIRECTIONS: *For each item below, think about the meaning of the underlined word from the Word List. Then, answer the question and explain your answer.*

1. If you leave garbage cans in front of your house all week, will they <u>ornament</u> your property?

_____

_____

2. The condor must have an <u>immensity</u> in which to fly. Can the condor survive in a small space?

_____

_____

B. DIRECTIONS: *Indicate whether each statement is* true *or* false. *Then, explain your answer.*

1. Colored lights and Chinese lanterns will *ornament* a backyard party.

T / F: _____ **Explanation:** _____

_____

2. An *immensity* can easily be fenced in.

T / F: _____ **Explanation:** _____

_____

C. DIRECTIONS: *Write the letter of the word that means* the same *or* about the same *as the vocabulary word.*

____ 1. ornament
    A. pollute   B. convince   C. decorate   D. detain

____ 2. immensity
    A. comedy   B. transition   C. tranquillity   D. vastness

Name _____ Date _____

Support for Writing a Plot Summary

Use this chart to take notes for a **plot summary** of "How the Snake Got Poison."

Plot Summary of "How the Snake Got Poison"

Setting:		
Major character God:		**Major character Snake:**
Main event from beginning of folk tale:	**Main event from middle of folk tale:**	**Main event from end of folk tale:**
Final outcome:		

Now, use your notes to write your **plot summary.** Be sure to include all the information called for on the chart.

"How the Snake Got Poison" by Zora Neale Hurston
Support for Extend Your Learning

Research and Technology

Use the following chart to take notes for the **feature article** you will write about Zora Neale Hurston. Focus on one aspect of her life that interests you. Look for a fact or detail that will grab your readers' attention. Look for phrases you can use as headings to emphasize main ideas. Finally, be sure every paragraph you write has a main idea and supporting details.

Topic:

Listening and Speaking

Use the following prompts as you work with a partner to gather unusual facts about an animal in preparation for a **story** you will make up and present to your classmates. Remember: You will not name the animal in your presentation.

Unusual fact 1: _____

Unusual fact 2: _____

Unusual fact 3: _____

Unusual fact 4: _____

Unusual fact 5: _____

Facial expressions, gestures, and movements that identify the animal: _____

_____

Dialogue: _____

_____

_____

_____

"How the Snake Got Poison" by Zora Neale Hurston
Enrichment: Snakes Are Not So Bad

You may have noticed that "How the Snake Got Poison" presents the snake somewhat sympathetically. Did that surprise you? Did you think that snakes were awful? Did you think they should all be stomped on by other animals or by human beings?

Actually, snakes have gotten a lot of what could be called bad press. That is, they have a bad reputation for no good reason. Yet many people fear or hate snakes. It may be that they believe myths about them that are simply not true.

Snake myth 1: Snakes are slimy.
Snake fact 1: Snakes are not slimy. They have scales, which serve as their skin. The scales are dry and either smooth or bumpy.

Snake myth 2: Snakes lie in wait to attack human beings.
Snake fact 2: Only a few snakes are particularly aggressive toward humans. Most snakes avoid humans at all costs because they know that humans may hurt them. Most poisonous snakes will strike at a person only when they are cornered, captured, or harassed in some way. The fact remains, however, that poisonous snakes are poisonous, and a snake's venom can kill. Of course, the venom is primarily used on other animals. Poisonous snakes use their poison to capture their prey.

Snake myth 3: Snakes are of no use and should be killed.
Snake fact 3: As "How the Snake Got Poison" implies, snakes have a place in the natural world. Snakes feed on the huge population of rats, mice, and other animals that eat corn, rice, and other crops and foods. Snake venom is used to make painkillers and treat snakebites. Snakes also play a part in the food chain, providing meals for hawks and other large hunting birds, mongooses, and bigger snakes.

Do some research on snakes. In an encyclopedia or on the Internet, find an illustration of a colorful snake. Find out where it lives, how it reproduces, and how long it lives.

DIRECTIONS: *In response to each myth, write a sentence that contradicts it. Be sure the information in your sentence is accurate.*

1. Snakes are dangerous to humans.

   _____

   _____

2. Snakes are useless.

   _____

   _____

3. Snakes are slimy.

   _____

   _____

"Sun and Moon in a Box" by Richard Erdoes and Alfonso Ortiz
"How the Snake Got Poison" by Zora Neale Hurston
Build Language Skills: Vocabulary

Idioms

An **idiomatic expression** is one in which the meaning of the expression is different from the meaning of the individual words that make up the expression. Idioms and idiomatic expressions are commonly used. We are so accustomed to hearing them that we may forget that they do not make sense if we take them literally. For example, if you have difficulty coming up with something to say to someone you have just met, it may be suggested that you find a way to *break the ice.* The suggestion has nothing to do with ice fishing or any other winter activity. It simply means "find a way to start a conversation."

A. DIRECTIONS: *Rewrite each of the following sentences. In place of the underlined idiomatic expression, use a* literal *expression, one whose meaning does* not *differ from the meaning of the individual words that make it up. If you are unsure of the meaning of an idiom, look it up in a dictionary (under the most important word in the expression) or on the Internet.*

1. The rudeness of the person who bumped into me in the mall was so extreme that I was <u>seeing red</u> for the next hour.

   _____

   _____

2. Anthony <u>made no bones about</u> his desire to win the science-fair competition.

   _____

Academic Vocabulary Practice

B. DIRECTIONS: *Answer each question using the underlined Academic Vocabulary word. Be sure to include the vocabulary word in your answer.*

1. Why do scientists <u>analyze</u> the results of an experiment?

   _____

2. What <u>aspect</u> of snakes might you do research on?

   _____

3. Which <u>detail</u> in "Sun and Moon in a Box" or "How the Snake Got Poison" did you particularly like?

   _____

4. What is a <u>unique characteristic</u> of a snake?

   _____

Unit 6 Resources: Themes in the Oral Tradition
137

Name _____ Date _____

"Sun and Moon in a Box" by Richard Erdoes and Alfonso Ortiz
"How the Snake Got Poison" by Zora Neale Hurston
Build Language Skills: Grammar

Capitalization

Capitalization is the use of uppercase letters (*A*, *B*, *C*, and so on). Capital letters signal the beginning of a sentence or a quotation and identify proper nouns and proper adjectives. **Proper nouns** include the names of people, geographical locations, specific events and time periods, organizations, languages, and religions. **Proper adjectives** are derived from proper nouns.

Use of Capital Letter	Example
Sentence beginning	The coyote was a bad swimmer. **H**e nearly drowned.
Quotation	The snake said, "**Y**ou know I'm down here in the dust."
Proper nouns	They traveled through the **S**outhwest.
Proper adjectives	Coyote might have run as far as the **M**exican border.

A. PRACTICE: *Rewrite each sentence below. Use capitalization correctly.*

1. the character named coyote suggested that they steal the box.

   _____

2. the folk tale takes place in the american southwest, perhaps in present-day arizona or new mexico.

   _____

   _____

3. coyote said to eagle, "this is a wonderful thing."

   _____

4. "i do not trust you," eagle said many times. "you will open that box."

   _____

B. Writing Application: *Write a short episode telling what Coyote might have done after he let the sun and the moon escape from the box. Include at least one quotation, one proper noun, and one proper adjective. Use capitalization correctly.*

   _____

   _____

   _____

   _____

   _____

"How the Snake Got Poison" by Zora Neale Hurston
Selection Test A

Critical Reading *Identify the letter of the choice that best answers the question.*

____ 1. Where does most of the dialogue in "How the Snake Got Poison" take place?
   A. in a desert
   B. in the heavens
   C. in a jungle
   D. on an ark

____ 2. According to "How the Snake Got Poison," why does God put the snake in the bushes?
   A. to kill all the other varmints
   B. to make the ground beautiful
   C. to act as God's bodyguard
   D. to keep the bushes trimmed

____ 3. According to "How the Snake Got Poison," after the snake gets poison, all the other varmints complain to God. Based on your reading of the selection, what can you infer is meant by *varmints*?
   A. rats and mice
   B. human beings
   C. other creatures
   D. other snakes

____ 4. According to "How the Snake Got Poison," how are the snakes and the other varmints alike?
   A. They all claim to be scared.
   B. They all change their shape.
   C. They all have feet.
   D. They all have claws.

____ 5. In "How the Snake Got Poison," what is the complaint of the other varmints when they go to see God?
   A. They are not as beautiful as the snake.
   B. There are not as plentiful as the snake.
   C. The snake is poisoning them.
   D. The snake is hunting them.

_____ 6. In "How the Snake Got Poison," what does the snake say in response to the other varmints' complaints?

    A. He cannot tell who is a friend and who is an enemy.

    B. He wants to be the most powerful varmint on earth.

    C. He wants snakes to be the only varmints on earth.

    D. He believes he is doing what God wants him to do.

_____ 7. According to "How the Snake Got Poison," how did snakes change after they got poison?

    A. Before, they were being killed; afterward, they were doing the killing.

    B. Before, they lived in the bushes; afterward, they lived in the trees.

    C. Before, they had no enemies; afterward, they had many enemies.

    D. Before, they hid in the bushes; afterward, they stayed in the open.

_____ 8. Who are the main characters in "How the Snake Got Poison"?

    A. the snake and the other varmints

    B. the snake and human beings

    C. God and all the varmints

    D. God and the snake

_____ 9. In "How the Snake Got Poison," what is God's final gift to the snake?

    A. fangs

    B. skin

    C. eyes

    D. rattles

_____ 10. As he is portrayed in "How the Snake Got Poison," which word best describes God?

    A. brutal

    B. vengeful

    C. reasonable

    D. strict

_____ 11. What cultural belief is reflected in "How the Snake Got Poison"?

    A. All creatures have a place on earth.

    B. Some creatures are superior to others.

    C. The rattlesnake is special.

    D. Rattlesnakes are untrustworthy.

___ 12. Which statement best describes a message of "How the Snake Got Poison"?

   A. The more you complain, the more likely you are to get what you want.

   B. Everyone deserves to be able to defend himself or herself.

   C. One needs a variety of tools to make it through life.

   D. There is basically an unfairness to life.

Vocabulary and Grammar

___ 13. Which of the following sentences uses the word *ornament* correctly?

   A. Intelligent replies will *ornament* any essay question.

   B. Stained-glass windows *ornament* the old church.

   C. Words of praise *ornament* the honored guest.

   D. Ghastly shrieks *ornament* the otherwise silent night.

___ 14. In which sentences is the capitalization correct?

   A. "Good morning, Michael." "how are you, Amanda?"

   B. "Good morning, michael." "How are you, amanda?"

   C. "good morning, michael." "how are you, amanda?"

   D. "Good morning, Michael." "How are you, Amanda?"

___ 15. In which sentence is the capitalization correct?

   A. Zora Neale Hurston was an important figure in the harlem renaissance.

   B. Zora neale hurston grew up in the small town of eatonville, Florida.

   C. Zora Neale Hurston collected folklore in Jamaica, Haiti, and Bermuda.

   D. Zora neale hurston's writing was popular but did not earn her a living.

Essay

16. What do you think of the snake in "How the Snake Got Poison"? Is he a sneaky character, or is he simply looking out for his own interests? Do you like him? Why or why not? In an essay, answer those questions. Mention at least one detail from the selection to support your opinion.

17. "How the Snake Got Poison" is written in dialect. It is a variation of a language in a certain region, and it has its own vocabulary, grammar, and pronunciation. In addition, the style of the writing is informal. In your opinion, do these characteristics have an overall effect on the selection? Would you have liked the selection better if it had not used dialect and an informal style? Why or why not? Express your opinion in an essay. Cite two examples from the selection to support your opinion.

"How the Snake Got Poison" by Zora Neale Hurston
Selection Test B

Critical Reading *Identify the letter of the choice that best completes the statement or answers the question.*

_____ 1. In "How the Snake Got Poison," how does the snake reach God?
A. by calling up to him
B. by climbing a ladder
C. by slithering through the bushes
D. by stomping over other varmints

_____ 2. According to "How the Snake Got Poison," why was the snake put in the bushes?
A. to monitor access to God
B. to tempt human beings
C. to make the ground beautiful
D. to catch objectionable animals

_____ 3. Before the snake first talks to God in "How the Snake Got Poison," what is his situation?
A. He cannot keep from being stomped to death.
B. He cannot find enough food to eat in the bushes.
C. He cannot move fast enough to hunt food to eat.
D. He cannot see God from his position in the bushes.

_____ 4. How might God best be described in "How the Snake Got Poison"?
A. standoffish
B. accessible
C. contemptuous
D. arrogant

_____ 5. From the setting of "How the Snake Got Poison," you can make inferences about the environment of the people who told the tale. Which of the following is the most likely environment?
A. extreme cold
B. a temperate woodland
C. a fishing community
D. a vast desert

_____ 6. What kind of character is the snake in "How the Snake Got Poison"?
A. an innocent, likable victim
B. an especially evil creature
C. a disrespectful, angry animal
D. a clever being who wants to survive

_____ 7. In what way are all the creatures in "How the Snake Got Poison" alike?
A. They all want to be powerful.
B. They all want to be warm.
C. They all want the snake to disappear.
D. They all want to protect themselves.

_____ 8. After God gives the snake poison in "How the Snake Got Poison," but before he responds to the other creatures' complaints, what is the basic contrast between the snake and the other creatures?
A. the place where they live
B. their closeness to God
C. their means of self-defense
D. the size of their families

_____ 9. In "How the Snake Got Poison," how does the snake change after he gets poison?
A. He goes from victim to victimizer.
B. He moves from the trees to the bushes.
C. He moves from the ground to the ladder.
D. He stops slithering and begins crawling.

_____ 10. Which passage from "How the Snake Got Poison" is most clearly an example of dialect?
A. "'God, you put me down here on my belly.'"
B. "God looked off towards immensity."
C. "So de snake took de poison in his mouf."
D. "God thought it over for a while."

_____ 11. In "How the Snake Got Poison," on what does God base the second decision he makes?
A. his annoyance with the snake
B. his anger at human beings
C. his fear that the animals will go to war
D. his desire for balance in the animal world

_____ 12. What does God do in "How the Snake Got Poison" to protect the other creatures from the snake?
A. He moves the snake to a deserted area.
B. He takes the poison from the snake.
C. He lectures the snake.
D. He gives the snake rattles.

_____ 13. What cultural belief is reflected in "How the Snake Got Poison"?
A. There is meant to be a balance in nature.
B. Some animals are sneakier than others.
C. Animals are smarter than human beings.
D. Always be careful walking through bushes.

_____ 14. What can you infer about the people who told "How the Snake Got Poison"?
A. They lived in a place with few bushes.
B. They lived in a place with many insects.
C. They were familiar with rattlesnakes.
D. They were familiar with garter snakes.

____ 15. Which statement best describes a message of "How the Snake Got Poison"?
  A. Life is fundamentally unfair.
  B. Self-protection is a key to survival.
  C. It is best to solve your problems by yourself.
  D. The more you know, the better able you are to deal with life.

Vocabulary and Grammar

____ 16. In which sentence is the meaning of the word *ornament* expressed?
  A. The snake was being tromped on by the other creatures.
  B. The snake was put on earth to make the ground beautiful.
  C. The snake complained to God about being stomped on.
  D. God gave the snake poison with which to defend himself.

____ 17. In which sentence is the meaning of the word *immensity* expressed?
  A. The poet considered the vastness of the universe.
  B. The intensity of the storm frightened the animals.
  C. The beauty of the landscape was incomparable.
  D. The scientist analyzed the results of her experiment.

____ 18. In which sentence is the capitalization correct?
  A. In 1925, Hurston headed for new York.
  B. There, she joined the harlem renaissance.
  C. Hurston was buried in an unmarked grave in Florida.
  D. Alice walker reawakened interest in Hurston's work.

Essay

19. In "How the Snake Got Poison," God hears the snake's plea, and then he hears the complaints of the other creatures. Finally, he hears the snake's response to those complaints. What is your opinion of all the animals' remarks? Is each argument valid? Are the animals just bickering among themselves? In an essay, state your opinion of each of the three arguments. Then, assess the solution. Might there have been a different way to solve the problem? If so, what is it?

20. In "How the Snake Got Poison," the animals call on God to resolve their dispute. In your opinion, why did they not work out their problems on their own? Why did they need the assistance of a third party? What do you think the animals' behavior says about human behavior? Respond to these questions in an essay. Cite at least two details from the selection or from your knowledge or experience to support your points.

21. How does "How the Snake Got Poison" illustrate the concept that nature must be kept in balance? At the beginning of the selection, what is out of balance? Why does God say, "You got to have some kind of protection"? How is the balance corrected? In an essay, answer these questions.

"The People Could Fly" by Virginia Hamilton
Vocabulary Warm-up Word Lists

Study these words from "The People Could Fly." Then, apply your knowledge to the activities that follow.

Word List A

babe [BAYB] *n.* an infant or baby
The tiny <u>babe</u> was nestled in his mother's arms.

firelight [FYER lyt] *n.* light from a fire
The <u>firelight</u> cozily cast pretty shadows on the walls.

flock [FLAHK] *n.* a large group of animals that usually stay together
The <u>flock</u> of geese landed on the pond.

hip [HIP] *adj.* located by someone's hip bone at the top of the leg
Myra's <u>hip</u> bandage covered the stitches she had received there.

horseback [HAWRS bak] *adv.* used with *on*, riding on a horse
Max thought it was fun to ride on <u>horseback</u> along the beach.

labored [LAY berd] *v.* worked, toiled
The students <u>labored</u> long hours over their group history project.

plantation [plan TAY shuhn] *n.* a large farm or estate
The Southern farmer grew peanuts on his <u>plantation</u>.

soothe [SOO*TH*] *v.* to calm or make better with gentle treatment
The quiet music will <u>soothe</u> your frazzled nerves.

Word List B

African [AF ri kuhn] *adj.* describing a person or thing from Africa
The <u>African</u> stone sculpture shows a graceful giraffe.

bawling [BAWL ing] *v.* crying or shouting noisily
When he fell, the toddler began <u>bawling</u> loudly.

bled [BLED] *v.* was bleeding or did bleed
The cut on her hand <u>bled</u> for only a short time.

clumsily [KLUHM zuh lee] *adv.* awkwardly, ungracefully
Anna moved <u>clumsily</u> on her skis until she took a lesson.

misery [MIZ uh ree] *n.* extreme unhappiness or sorrow
The <u>misery</u> Rob felt when he had the flu could be seen on his face.

slavery [SLAY vuh ree] *n.* owning human beings as property
<u>Slavery</u> in the United States ended during the Civil War.

souls [SOHLZ] *n.* people
Only one hundred <u>souls</u> lived in the small village.

sundown [SUHN down] *n.* the time of the day when the sun sets
At <u>sundown</u>, red and pink clouds filled the sky.

Name _____ Date _____

"The People Could Fly" by Virginia Hamilton
Vocabulary Warm-up Exercises

Exercise A *Fill in each blank in the paragraph below with an appropriate word from Word List A. Use each word only once.*

Donna and her friends liked to go camping on land that used to be part of an

old cotton [1] _____. During the day, they loved to go riding on

[2] _____. At dinnertime, they [3] _____ together to cook

a good meal. Then, after dark, they would sit around the campfire, huddled close to

each other like a [4] _____ of sheep, while the [5] _____

played upon their faces. Donna would pull out a book of scary stories from the

[6] _____ pocket of her jeans. She read one story that made one of her

friends wail like a little [7] _____. To [8] _____ him, the

group decided to start toasting marshmallows!

Exercise B *Decide whether each statement below is true or false. Circle T or F. Then, explain your answer.*

1. One who studies <u>African</u> folk tales probably knows a lot about Africa.
   T / F _____

2. If Carol always moves <u>clumsily</u>, then she ice skates well.
   T / F _____

3. If Don cut his hand while dicing onions, he <u>bled</u>.
   T / F _____

4. The expression "<u>misery</u> loves company" means it makes people feel better when
   they know others are feeling good.
   T / F _____

5. If many <u>souls</u> attended the meeting, a lot of people were there.
   T / F _____

6. It is nice to wake up early to watch the <u>sundown</u>.
   T / F _____

7. If someone is <u>bawling</u>, he or she is not very happy.
   T / F _____

8. <u>Slavery</u> provided plantation owners with workers in the South.
   T / F _____

Name _____ Date _____

"The People Could Fly" by Virginia Hamilton
Reading Warm-up A

Read the following passage. Pay special attention to the underlined words. Then, read it again, and complete the activities. Use a separate sheet of paper for your written answers.

My name is Rob, and my parents were slaves on a cotton <u>plantation</u> in Mississippi. I was born there, so I was a slave, too. My mama told me that when I was a <u>babe</u>, she was not given enough time to care for me. Instead, she was sent back to the fields to work. The night was her favorite time, for then we were together again. She would hold me in her arms. There in the glow and warmth of the <u>firelight</u>, she softly sang lullabies to me.

They were the bits of songs she could remember from Africa, her homeland. She couldn't sing the words loudly, for to use her native language was forbidden by the plantation owner.

When I got older, and my sister was born, I remember how my mother carried her in a sort of <u>hip</u> cloth tied to her body like a sling. Being carried that way was the only thing that could <u>soothe</u> that baby when she cried.

As a young boy, I was sent to pick cotton. The overseer rode up to our cabins on <u>horseback</u> every morning with a whip in his hand. With rough words, he told us to get moving. Like a <u>flock</u> of birds or animals, not like the people we were, we headed to the fields.

Picking cotton was hard, hot work. It cut our hands. We <u>labored</u> long hours. Sometimes we sang songs to keep our spirits alive. We disguised the words of these songs. The overseer didn't know those songs were from African music. It was our secret, and it was a way we stayed connected to the land from which we had been taken.

We had stories, too. They came from Africa, but parts of them got changed, because slaves were forbidden to practice their native culture. We were proud of our stories, though. They told of tricksters and heroes, and they were our way of keeping our roots alive.

1. Circle the word that tells the kind of <u>plantation</u> on which Rob grew up. Define *plantation*.

2. Circle the words that tell what Rob's mother told him about the time when he was a <u>babe</u>. What has a family member told you about the time when you were a *babe*?

3. Underline the words that describe the <u>firelight</u>. Use *firelight* in a sentence.

4. Circle the words that explain why Rob's mother wore a <u>hip</u> cloth tied to her body. Define *hip*.

5. Underline the words that tell what could <u>soothe</u> the boy's baby sister. What can *soothe* you?

6. Circle the words that tell who rode on <u>horseback</u>. Use *horseback* in a sentence.

7. Underline the words that tell what kind of <u>flock</u> it felt like to Rob. What is a *flock*?

8. Underline the words that tell more about how the slaves <u>labored</u> long hours. What is something at which you have *labored*?

Name _____ Date _____

"The People Could Fly" by Virginia Hamilton
Reading Warm-up B

Read the following passage. Pay special attention to the underlined words. Then, read it again, and complete the activities. Use a separate sheet of paper for your written answers.

During the period of time from the 1500s to the 1800s, large numbers of African people were captured by slave traders. These unfortunate souls were shipped like cargo, under terrible conditions. They were taken to the West Indies and to the Americas to be sold into slavery.

Slave traders realized there was a great need for cheap labor in the West Indian and British colonies. They saw the taking of Africans as a way to fill this need and to profit by it.

Most of the captives came from West Africa. Some were captured in battle with other tribes and sold to the slave traders in exchange for goods. The majority of those who became slaves, however, were kidnapped from their villages by the slave traders. The traders usually chose the strongest individuals because they were more likely to survive the terrible journey. The captives' freedom and their culture were savagely stripped away from them. Imagine their misery as they realized they would never see another sunrise or sundown as a free man or woman.

The route of some slave ships ended in the American south in big cities such as New Orleans. There, the slaves were sold. Other voyages took a triangular journey. They set off from New England colonies, carrying rum to be traded in Africa. Next, slaves were taken to the West Indies and traded for sugar and molasses. This cargo, in turn, was taken to New England to be sold to the rum makers.

It is believed that one third of the captives died during the horrible crossings. They were mercilessly chained together, causing them to move clumsily. Those who rebelled were beaten or whipped until they bled. Unclean conditions and lack of food caused much illness, and the bawling of the suffering captives could be heard. The survivors went on to endure more hardships as slaves.

1. Underline the words that tell what happened to large numbers of African people. Use *African* in a sentence.

2. Circle the words that describe what happened to these unfortunate souls. Define *souls*.

3. Circle the sentences that explain why the slave traders wanted to capture Africans to be sold into slavery. Why is *slavery* wrong?

4. Underline the words that suggest why the captives felt misery. What is *misery*?

5. The story says that the slaves never experienced another sundown as free people. What does this mean?

6. Circle the words that tell why the slaves moved clumsily. Have you ever moved *clumsily*? Explain.

7. Underline the words that tell why some slaves bled. Use *bled* in a sentence.

8. Circle the words that tell why the slaves' bawling could be heard. Define *bawling*.

Name _____ Date _____

Reading: Use a Venn Diagram to Compare and Contrast

When you **compare and contrast,** you recognize similarities and differences. You can compare and contrast elements in a literary work by **using a Venn diagram** to examine character traits, situations, and ideas. First, reread the text to locate the details you will compare. Then, write the details on a diagram like the ones shown below. Recording these details will help you understand the similarities and differences in a literary work.

DIRECTIONS: *Fill in the Venn diagrams as directed to make comparisons about elements of "The People Could Fly."*

1. Compare Toby and Sarah. Write characteristics of Toby in the left-hand oval and characteristics of Sarah in the right-hand oval. Write characteristics that they share in the overlapping part of the two ovals.

Toby   **Both**   **Sarah**

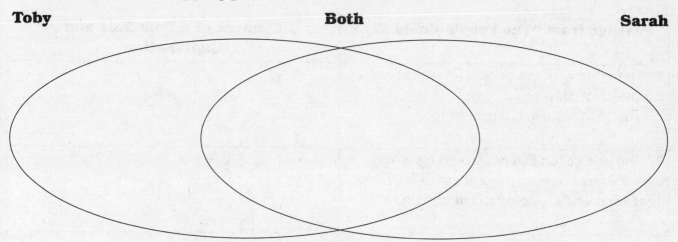

2. Compare the enslaved people with the Overseer and Driver. Write characteristics of the enslaved people in the left-hand oval and characteristics of the Overseer and Driver in the right-hand oval. Write characteristics that they share in the overlapping part of the two ovals.

Enslaved People   **Both**   **Overseer and Driver**

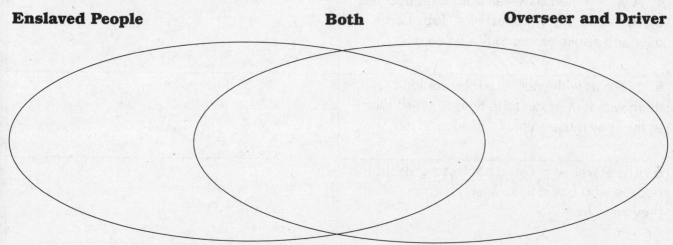

Name _____ Date _____

"The People Could Fly" by Virginia Hamilton
Literary Analysis: Folk Tale

A **folk tale** is a story that is composed orally and then passed from person to person by word of mouth. Although folk tales originate in this **oral tradition,** many of them are eventually collected and written down. Similar folk tales are told by different cultures throughout the world. Such folk tales have common character types, plot elements, and themes. Folk tales often teach a lesson about life and present a clear separation between good and evil. Folk tales are part of the oral tradition that also includes fairy tales, legends, myths, fables, tall tales, and ghost stories.

DIRECTIONS: *Read each passage from "The People Could Fly." In the second column of the chart, indicate whether the passage* teaches a lesson about life *or whether it* clearly presents good, clearly presents evil, *or presents a clear distinction between the two. Then, explain your choice. Tell why you think the example shows the element you have chosen.*

Passage from "The People Could Fly"	Element of a Folk Tale and Explanation
1. Then, many of the people [in Africa] were captured for Slavery. . . . The folks were full of misery, then.	
2. The one called Driver cracked his whip over the slow ones to make them move faster. That whip was a slice-open cut of pain.	
3. The . . . woman fell to the earth. The old man that was there, Toby, came and helped her to her feet.	
4. A young man slave fell from the heat. The Driver come and whipped him. Toby come over and spoke words to the fallen one.	
5. "Take us with you!" . . . Toby couldn't take them with him. Hadn't the time to teach them to fly. They must wait for a chance to run.	
6. The slaves who could not fly told about the people who could fly to their children. When they were free.	

Name _____ Date _____

"The People Could Fly" by Virginia Hamilton
Vocabulary Builder

Word List

scorned	croon	shuffle

A. DIRECTIONS: *For each item below, think about the meaning of the underlined word from the Word List. Then, answer the question, and explain your answer.*

1. The workers were so <u>scorned</u> by the company owner that they protested. Were they right to protest?

   _____

2. The popular singer will <u>croon</u> the audience's favorite song. What kind of song will the singer perform?

   _____

3. The clowns <u>shuffle</u> across the stage. How are they moving?

   _____

B. DIRECTIONS: *Indicate whether each statement is* true *or* false. *Then, explain your answer.*

1. A well-loved teacher is one who is very much *scorned.*

   T / F: _____ **Explanation:** _____

   _____

2. A singer is likely to *croon* a love song.

   T / F: _____ **Explanation:** _____

   _____

3. A person taking a power walk is likely to *shuffle.*

   T / F: _____ **Explanation:** _____

   _____

C. DIRECTIONS: *Write the letter of the word or group of words that means the opposite of the vocabulary word.*

____ 1. scorned
   A. commanded   B. resigned   C. appreciated   D. hired

____ 2. croon
   A. sing softly   B. speak quietly   C. speak haltingly   D. sing loudly

Name _____ Date _____

"The People Could Fly" by Virginia Hamilton
Support for Writing a Review

Use this chart to take notes for a **review** of "The People Could Fly."

Notes for Review of "The People Could Fly" by Virginia Hamilton

Element of the Tale	My Opinion of the Element	Details from the Tale That Support My Opinion
Characters		
Description		
Dialogue		
Plot		

Now, write a draft of your review. Tell readers whether or not you think they will enjoy "The People Could Fly." Remember to support your opinions with details from the tale.

Name _____ Date _____

"The People Could Fly" by Virginia Hamilton
Support for Extend Your Learning

Research and Technology

Use this chart as you do **research** on a coded slave song. In the first and third columns, write words or phrases from the song that serve as a code, and in the second and fourth columns, write the literal meaning of the words or phrases.

Word or Phrase	Meaning	Word or Phrase	Meaning

Listening and Speaking

Use the following prompts to prepare a **television news report** on the amazing events that took place in "The People Could Fly." Respond to the prompts with details from the folk tale.

Where events took place: _____

When events took place: _____

What happened: _____

_____

Question for eyewitness: _____

_____

Eyewitness's answer: _____

_____

Question for eyewitness: _____

_____

Eyewitness's answer: _____

_____

Question for eyewitness: _____

_____

Eyewitness's answer: _____

_____

Name _____ Date _____

"The People Could Fly" by Virginia Hamilton
Enrichment: Oral Tradition

There is probably not a society in history that has not had an oral tradition. Before there was writing, there were stories. Those stories did not die out when the people who made them up died. Instead, people repeated their stories to an audience—perhaps their children, perhaps other people in their community. They told their stories over and over again. Eventually, the members of the audience committed the stories to memory. At last, they were able to repeat the stories to their own audiences.

You probably already have the beginnings of an oral tradition committed to memory. Have you told the same story to more than one friend? Have you heard stories from others in your family that you could repeat? How about song lyrics? How many of those have you memorized? Have you memorized any poems? Have you memorized a part for a play? Can you quote dialogue from your favorite movie or television show? All of those might be the start of your own oral tradition.

Now, think about adding a folk tale to the mix.

DIRECTIONS: *Follow these steps to commit a folk tale to memory.*

1. Choose a folk tale that you are particularly fond of—"The People Could Fly" or another folk tale in your textbook, or one you have read on your own. Be sure it is short—no more than two or three pages.

2. You will probably not be able to memorize the entire folk tale in one day. So, divide it into sections for example,—five sections, one for every day of a week of school.

3. Each day, work on one section. Read it over and over again. Read it to yourself, and then read it aloud. On the chart below, make some notes of key events or key phrases. The important thing, however, is to *read and repeat,* not to write.

4. Do not try to memorize every word. Concentrate on repeating the key events and the key lines of dialogue in each section.

5. After the first day, review the previous days' sections before starting on that day's section.

6. Once you become comfortable with the process, ask a classmate, friend, or family member to be your audience.

Section 1	Section 2	Section 3	Section 4	Section 5

Name _____ Date _____

"The People Could Fly" by Virginia Hamilton
Selection Test A

Critical Reading *Identify the letter of the choice that best answers the question.*

_____ 1. According to "The People Could Fly," when did the people first fly?
   A. when they lived in Africa long ago
   B. when they were on the boat from Africa
   C. when they were enslaved in America
   D. when they escaped from slavery

_____ 2. According to "The People Could Fly," why did the people at one time shed their wings?
   A. They preferred sailing to flying.
   B. The slave ship had no room for wings.
   C. They no longer knew the magic.
   D. They knew they could never escape.

_____ 3. In "The People Could Fly," why is the one called Master compared to a piece of coal?
   A. He works in a mine.
   B. He uses coal in his fireplace.
   C. He is hard and unyielding.
   D. He is black like his slaves.

_____ 4. A folk tale may have villains and heroes. Who are the villains in "The People Could Fly"?
   I.   the one called Master
   II. Toby
   III. the Driver
   IV. Sarah
   V.   the Overseer
   A. I, II, IV
   B. II, IV, V
   C. II, III, IV
   D. I, III, V

_____ 5. In "The People Could Fly," how are Toby and Sarah alike?
   A. They are slaves with children.
   B. They are slaves who wish to escape.
   C. They are slaves who are old.
   D. They know magic words.

_____ 6. Which character in "The People Could Fly" says the magic words?

    A. the Overseer

    B. Toby

    C. the Driver

    D. Sarah

_____ 7. Folk tales often show a clear difference between good and evil. In "The People Could Fly," which two elements or characters represent that difference?

    A. freedom and slavery

    B. Toby and Sarah

    C. the magic words and the wings

    D. the one called Master and the Driver

_____ 8. Which of these characters is most different from Toby in "The People Could Fly"?

    A. Sarah

    B. Sarah's child

    C. the Overseer

    D. the other slaves

_____ 9. In "The People Could Fly," Toby does not fly until the end of the folk tale. Which statement best explains why he does not fly away sooner?

    A. He no longer has wings.

    B. He is too old to fly far.

    C. He cannot remember the magic words.

    D. He wants to help other slaves escape.

_____ 10. In "The People Could Fly," what does flying stand for?

    A. going to market

    B. going to church

    C. escaping to freedom

    D. dreaming about birds

_____ 11. In "The People Could Fly," Toby's magic words allow slaves to fly, yet he does not say the words to everyone. What lesson is taught when Toby leaves a group of slaves waiting for a chance to run?

    A. Toby will come back for them before long.

    B. Toby is not as powerful as the Overseer.

    C. Not all the slaves can hear the magic words.

    D. People escaped from slavery in different ways.

___ 12. How does a folk tale such as "The People Could Fly" usually come to be?
   A. It is written down by hand.
   B. It is made up by a group of people.
   C. It is passed down by word of mouth.
   D. It is published in paperback form.

___ 13. Why would a folk tale such as "The People Could Fly" have been important to people living in slavery?
   A. It gave them hope.
   B. It showed them how to work faster.
   C. It told them how to avoid the Driver.
   D. It reminded them of Africa.

Vocabulary and Grammar

___ 14. In which sentence is the meaning of the word *scorned* expressed?
   A. Toby remembered the magic words.
   B. The slaves hated being looked down on.
   C. Master was a hard, unfeeling man.
   D. Sarah's baby would not stop crying.

___ 15. What does the abbreviation stand for in this sentence?
   Virginia Hamilton held a B.A. from Antioch College.

   A. barium
   B. Buenos Aires
   C. batting average
   D. bachelor of arts

Essay

16. In "The People Could Fly," how are Toby and the Overseer different? What is each character like? What characteristics does each one represent? In an essay, compare the two characters, showing their differences. Cite two details from the selection to support your main ideas.

17. "The People Could Fly" takes places during the time of slavery in America. In your opinion, what lesson about slavery does the folk tale teach? What lesson about freedom does it teach? State your ideas in an essay. Support your points with two references to the selection.

Name _____   Date _____

"The People Could Fly" by Virginia Hamilton
Selection Test B

Critical Reading *Identify the letter of the choice that best completes the statement or answers the question.*

____ 1. According to "The People Could Fly," what is the source of the people's ability to fly?
   A. helium
   B. wings
   C. magic
   D. dreams

____ 2. In "The People Can Fly," why do the slaves describe the so-called Master as "a hard lump of clay"?
   A. He owns a quarry.
   B. He manufactures pottery.
   C. He refuses to change.
   D. He is muscular.

____ 3. In "The People Could Fly," how are the Overseer and the Driver alike?
   I.   They work for the so-called Master.
   II. They can speak the magic words.
   III. They wish to help Sarah and her baby.
   IV. They behave cruelly toward the people.
   A. I and III
   B. II and IV
   C. II and III
   D. I and IV

____ 4. According to "The People Could Fly," why does Sarah keep working even though her baby is crying?
   A. The Overseer will whip them if she stops.
   B. She does not know how to comfort the baby.
   C. She needs to earn money so she can feed the baby.
   D. The so-called Master will sell the baby if she stops.

____ 5. In "The People Could Fly," why does Sarah tell Toby that she must go soon?
   A. She and her baby are being whipped.
   B. She and her baby are hungry for lunch.
   C. She misses her homeland and family.
   D. She wants to raise her child in Africa.

____ 6. What is the most important difference between Toby and the Overseer in "The People Could Fly"?
   A. One is skilled, and one is unskilled.
   B. One is elderly, and one is young.
   C. One is white, and one is black.
   D. One is cruel, and one is kind.

___ 7. What role does Toby play in "The People Could Fly"?
A. He encourages the people to work.
B. He helps certain people care for their children.
C. He helps certain people fly away.
D. He teaches the people to accept slavery.

___ 8. What is an important distinction among the slaves in "The People Could Fly"?
A. Some work in the fields, and some work in the house.
B. Some still have the power to fly, and some do not.
C. Some have children, and some do not.
D. Some trust Toby, and some do not.

___ 9. According to "The People Could Fly," what does Toby hope will become of the slaves who do not go with him?
A. They will persuade the so-called Master to treat them better.
B. They will learn how to fly and escape on their own.
C. They will gain their freedom by running away.
D. They will plan and carry out an uprising.

___ 10. In "The People Could Fly," why does the one who calls himself Master say that the escape is a lie?
A. He does not believe the Overseer's story about flying slaves.
B. He is sure that all the slaves will return to work the next day.
C. He thinks that he must have miscounted the slaves on his estate.
D. He does not want to admit that he has been fooled by Toby.

___ 11. In "The People Could Fly," which two elements or characters represent a clear distinction between good and evil?
A. blackbirds and eagles
B. slavery and freedom
C. the Master and the Overseer
D. wings and magic

___ 12. What does Toby most likely represent in "The People Could Fly"?
A. the people's wish to return to Africa
B. the people's wish to live in freedom
C. the people's wish to be treated fairly
D. the people's wish to have a better Master

___ 13. What lesson about life is taught by "The People Could Fly"?
A. Africans who were enslaved brought magic with them.
B. It was possible to escape from slavery if you knew magic.
C. Cruel people get more out of workers than kind people.
D. When conditions are bad, it is essential to keep hope alive.

_____ 14. Which of the following topics is essential to the message of "The People Could Fly"?
  A. the importance of using magic wisely
  B. the triumph of freedom over slavery
  C. the commitment to being a good worker
  D. the importance of being a good mother

_____ 15. How does a folk tale such as "The People Could Fly" originate?
  A. It begins as an oral tradition.
  B. It begins as a cave painting.
  C. It appears in a collection of folk tales.
  D. It is generated by computer software.

Vocabulary and Grammar

_____ 16. In which sentence does the word *scorned* make sense?
  A. Sarah found herself *scorned* by Toby as he said the magic words.
  B. The people were so *scorned* by the Overseer that they hated him.
  C. The people on the slave ship *scorned* each other in order to survive.
  D. Toby *scorned* the people so that they would be able to fly away.

_____ 17. In which sentence is the meaning of the word *croon* expressed?
  A. The baby grew quiet when Sarah sang and hummed soothingly.
  B. The Overseer snarled at the people to make them work faster.
  C. Toby encouraged the people to believe that they could fly.
  D. The baby whimpered and fussed while Sarah worked.

_____ 18. In which sentence does the word *shuffle* make sense?
  A. The people *shuffled* as they flew over the land to freedom.
  B. The Driver *shuffled* toward the people and cracked his whip.
  C. Sarah *shuffled* slowly as the Overseer criticized her work.
  D. The people *shuffled* around each other as they danced.

_____ 19. Which of the following abbreviations is correct?
  A. Mr for *Mister*
  B. M.B.A. for *master of business administration*
  C. mr. for *meter*
  D. M.A. for *Massachusetts*

Essay

20. Why might enslaved Africans have told a folk tale like "The People Could Fly"? Might it have served as a comfort? As an inspiration? Might it have served some other purpose? Express your thoughts in an essay. Cite two details from the selection to support your main ideas.

21. If Toby is an example of an African who has not forgotten about flying despite the oppression of slavery, what does Sarah represent? In an essay, contrast Toby and Sarah. Show how they are alike and how they are different.

Vocabulary Warm-up Word Lists

Study these words from "All Stories Are Anansi's." Then, apply your knowledge to the activities that follow.

Word List A

accepted [ak SEPT ed] *v.* taken something that is offered
   Donna graciously <u>accepted</u> the compliment.

offering [AWF er ing] *v.* asking someone if he or she would take something
   Linda was <u>offering</u> the guests cake while I poured lemonade.

opinion [uh PIN yuhn] *n.* belief about a particular subject
   In Jeremy's <u>opinion</u>, a cell phone is a nuisance.

protect [pruh TEKT] *v.* to keep safe
   We must <u>protect</u> the environment.

respect [ri SPEKT] *n.* a feeling of admiration or consideration
   In Japan, people show great <u>respect</u> to their elders.

therefore [*THAIR* for] *adv.* for that reason
   The tiger was wounded and <u>therefore</u> more dangerous.

Word List B

accustomed [uh KUS tuhmd] *adj.* used to something
   Americans are <u>accustomed</u> to having many choices.

acknowledge [ak NAHL ij] *v.* to accept that something is true
   Most people <u>acknowledge</u> that the Internet has changed our lives.

dispute [dis PYOOT] *n.* a serious argument or disagreement
   The worker <u>dispute</u> over wages ended in a strike.

prisoner [PRIZ uhn ner] *n.* someone who is taken and held by force
   The guard locked the <u>prisoner</u> in a tiny cell.

prowling [PROWL ing] *v.* quietly moving around on the hunt
   We heard the bear <u>prowling</u> outside the cabin, looking for food.

warriors [WOR ee erz] *n.* experienced and skillful soldiers
   We honor our nation's <u>warriors</u> on Veterans Day.

Name _____ Date _____

"All Stories Are Anansi's" by Harold Courlander
Vocabulary Warm-up Exercises

Exercise A *Fill in each blank in the paragraph below with an appropriate word from Word List A. Use each word only once.*

Doris [1] _____ the invitation to go to the concert, but only out of

[2] _____ for her mother who loved classical music. She knew her

mom was [3] _____ her an opportunity to enjoy "finer things," but

in Doris's [4] _____, classical music was a waste of time. To

[5] _____ her mom's feelings, Doris acted like she really loved the

performance. [6] _____, she wasn't terribly surprised when her mom

invited her to another concert the following month.

Exercise B *Find a synonym for each word in the following vocabulary list. Use each synonym in a sentence that makes the meaning of the word clear.*

Example: prowling **Synonym**: *raiding*
  When I heard a noise in the middle of the night, I knew my brother was <u>raiding</u> the kitchen for a snack.

1. dispute   **Synonym:** _____
  _____

2. prisoner   **Synonym:** _____
  _____

3. acknowledge   **Synonym:** _____
  _____

4. accustomed   **Synonym:** _____
  _____

5. warriors   **Synonym:** _____
  _____

Name _____ Date _____

"All Stories Are Anansi's" by Harold Courlander
Reading Warm-up A

Read the following passage. Pay special attention to the underlined words. Then, read it again, and complete the activities. Use a separate sheet of paper for your written answers.

Storytelling is as old as language. In times past, storytellers were the keepers of folklore. Some cultures accepted these tellers of tales as a gift from the gods. Adults, as well as children, eagerly gathered around the storyteller to hear the stories they knew by heart. Usually the storyteller had a trick or two that would take the audience by surprise, but not too often. It was the repetition of the familiar words that audiences loved. Today, many people have the opinion that storytelling is just for children. They forget the time when everyone joined the story circle.

We all have a need for stories. Our stories are everywhere: in conversations, newspapers, television, and films. Each kind of story fulfills a special need. Stories from folklore fulfill a need, too. Storyteller Tim Sheppard tells us, "Every effort to explain shared customs and values needs a tale. Every bit of wisdom is best expressed by a story." In other words, the values and wisdom of our culture are preserved in our lore. Traditional tales teach us about ourselves by offering insights into what we as a group admire and fear. For this reason, we respect our folk stories. We continue to protect and preserve them to keep them from dying out. Today, as in the past, the storyteller helps us do this.

Listening to a live storyteller is a unique experience. Like a spinning spider, the storyteller traps you in a web of words and holds you captive. The teller spins and spins, until the world of the story is fully formed. Yet, each listener imagines the world in a personal way, therefore creating a unique universe in his or her own mind.

So, look for the storytellers in your area. Enter the circle where storytelling is for all. The stories you will hear are timeless, meaningful, and meant only for listening.

1. Underline the words that tell how cultures accepted tellers of tales. Write a sentence using the word *accepted*.

2. Underline the words that give the opinion of many people. Write your *opinion* on another subject.

3. Underline the words that tell what traditional tales are offering. Rewrite the sentence using a synonym for *offering*.

4. Circle the words that tell what we respect. Write the meaning of *respect*.

5. Circle the words that tell from what we protect our folk stories. Write about something you think your community should *protect* and preserve.

6. Underline the words that tell what, therefore, creates a unique universe. Write a sentence using the word *therefore*.

163

Name _____ Date _____

"All Stories Are Anansi's" by Harold Courlander
Reading Warm-up B

Read the following passage. Pay special attention to the underlined words. Then, read it again, and complete the activities. Use a separate sheet of paper for your written answers.

If it weren't for spiders, we would all be dead. This sounds like an exaggeration, but it probably isn't. If it weren't for spiders, the insects and other small critters that carry animal diseases and destroy food crops would eventually overrun the world. Though some may <u>dispute</u> this claim, people who study these things <u>acknowledge</u> that spiders do keep the insect population in check. How do they do it? Well, spiders eat a lot, and there are a lot of them. In just one acre of meadowland, there can be as many as two million hungry spiders.

Saving the world is a big job. It requires extraordinary weapons and skills. Luckily, the W.A.S. (World Army of Spiders) has both. Spider weapons include silk, stealth, and venom. Spider skills include the ability to spin, spit, jump, pounce, mimic, dive, fish, lasso, cast nets, fly through the air, and walk on water.

You are <u>accustomed</u> to seeing spiders spin webs to trap their victims. Have you ever seen the Ogre-faced Spider cast its small flat web down upon its prey and hold it <u>prisoner</u>? You are used to seeing spiders <u>prowling</u> around in the dirt. Have you ever seen a Fishing Spider run across the surface of water? The Bolas Spider spins a line beaded with sticky droplets. It throws the line like a lasso and when the glue sticks to a victim, the spider hauls it in. The Trap Door Spider hides underground beneath a trap door lined with silk. The Water Spider hides underwater inside an air bubble made of silk. The Ant Mimic Spider fools its enemies by mimicking the ants with which it lives.

Spider <u>warriors</u> around the world are secretly watching, silently capturing, and steadily devouring the earth's smallest enemies.

Aren't you glad they are?

1. Circle the words that tell what some people may <u>dispute</u>. Rewrite the sentence using a synonym for **dispute**.

2. Underline the words that tell what some people <u>acknowledge</u>. Write the meaning of **acknowledge**.

3. Circle the words that mean the same as <u>accustomed</u>. Write a sentence about something you are **accustomed** to seeing.

4. Underline the words that tell how the Ogre-faced Spider holds its prey <u>prisoner</u>. Give a synonym for **prisoner**.

5. Underline the words that tell where spiders are seen <u>prowling</u>. Name two places where you might find spiders **prowling**.

6. Underline the words that tell what spider <u>warriors</u> are doing. Name a famous group of **warriors** you've studied or read about.

Name _____ Date _____

"All Stories Are Anansi's" by Harold Courlander

Reading: Use a Venn Diagram to Compare and Contrast

When you **compare and contrast,** you recognize similarities and differences. You can compare and contrast elements in a literary work by **using a Venn diagram** to examine character traits, situations, and ideas. First, reread the text to locate the details you will compare. Then, write the details on a diagram like the ones shown below. Recording these details will help you understand the similarities and differences in a literary work.

DIRECTIONS: *Fill in the Venn diagrams as directed to make comparisons about elements of "All Stories Are Anansi's."*

1. Compare Anansi and Onini, the great python. Write characteristics of Anansi in the left-hand oval and characteristics of Onini in the right-hand oval. Write characteristics that they share in the overlapping part of the two ovals.

Anansi   **Both**   **Onini**

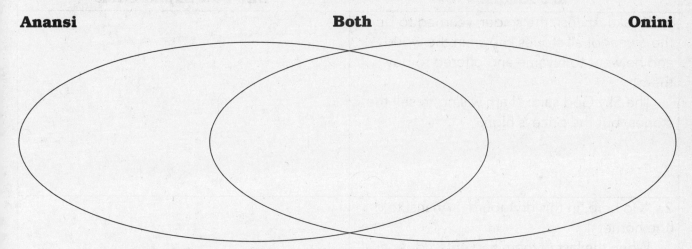

2. Compare Mmoboro, the hornets, with Osebo, the leopard. Write characteristics of the hornets in the left-hand oval and characteristics of the leopard in the right-hand oval. Write characteristics that they share in the overlapping part of the two ovals.

Hornets   **Both**   **Leopard**

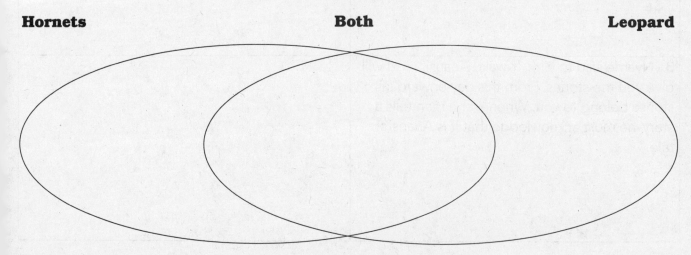

Name _____ Date _____

"All Stories Are Anansi's" by Harold Courlander
Literary Analysis: Folk Tale

   A **folk tale** is a story that is composed orally and then passed from person to person by word of mouth. Although folk tales originate in this **oral tradition,** many of them are eventually collected and written down. Similar folk tales are told by different cultures throughout the world. Such folk tales have common character types, plot elements, and themes. Folk tales often teach a lesson about life and present a clear separation between good and evil. Folk tales are part of the oral tradition that also includes fairy tales, legends, myths, fables, tall tales, and ghost stories.

DIRECTIONS: *Read each passage from "All Stories Are Anansi's." In the second column of the chart, indicate what value or lesson about life the passage teaches. Then, explain your choice.*

Passage from "All Stories Are Anansi's"	Value or Lesson About Life and Explanation
1. Kwaku Anansi, the spider, yearned to be the owner of all stories known in the world, and he went to Nyame and offered to buy them. The Sky God said: "I am willing to sell the stories, but the price is high."	
2. "Go here, in this dry gourd," Anansi told [the hornets]. . . . When the last of them had entered, Anansi plugged the hole with a ball of grass, saying: "Oh, yes, but you are really foolish people!"	
3. Nyame said to him: "Kwaku Anansi, . . . I will give you the stories. From this day onward, all stories belong to you. Whenever a man tells a story, he must acknowledge that it is Anansi's tale."	

Name _____ Date _____

"All Stories Are Anansi's" by Harold Courlander
Vocabulary Builder

Word List

yearned   gourd   acknowledge

A. DIRECTIONS: *For each item below, think about the meaning of the underlined word from the Word List. Then, answer the question, and explain your answer.*

1. The hornets probably <u>yearned</u> to play a trick on Anansi. Did they want very much to get back at him?

    _____

2. A <u>gourd</u> was put on the table when dinner was served. For what would the gourd be used?

    _____

3. Will you <u>acknowledge</u> Anansi as the owner of every story you tell?

    _____

B. DIRECTIONS: *Indicate whether each statement is* true *or* false. *Then, explain your answer.*

1. You *yearn* for something you do not want.

    T / F: _____ **Explanation:** _____

    _____

2. It would be appropriate to serve water in a *gourd*.

    T / F: _____ **Explanation:** _____

    _____

3. You can *acknowledge* someone by ignoring him or her.

    T / F: _____ **Explanation:** _____

    _____

C. DIRECTIONS: *Write the letter of the word that means the same or about the same as the vocabulary word.*

____ 1. yearned
   A. rejected   B. questioned   C. desired   D. ignored

____ 2. gourd
   A. cup   B. fork   C. platter   D. knife

____ 3. acknowledge
   A. taunt   B. challenge   C. credit   D. dismiss

Name _____ Date _____

"All Stories Are Anansi's" by Harold Courlander
Support for Writing a Review

Use this chart to take notes for a **review** of "All Stories Are Anansi's."

Notes for Review of "All Stories Are Anansi's" by Harold Courlander

Element of the Tale	My Opinion of the Element	Details From the Tale That Support My Opinion
Characters		
Description		
Dialogue		
Plot		

Now, write a draft of your review. Tell readers whether or not you think they will enjoy "All Stories Are Anansi's." Remember to support your opinions with details from the tale.

Name _____ Date _____

Support for Extend Your Learning

Research and Technology

Use this chart as you do **research** on tropical spiders of western Africa. Once you have completed your research, use your notes to prepare written descriptions and drawings with captions. Share your findings with your class.

Types	Physical Features	Diet	Life Cycle	Habitat	Behaviors

Listening and Speaking

Use the following prompts to prepare a **television news report** about Anansi's amazing deeds. Respond to the prompts with details from "All Stories Are Anansi's."

Where events took place: _____

_____

When events took place: _____

What Anansi wanted: _____

What happened with the hornets: _____

_____

What happened with the python: _____

_____

What happened with the leopard: _____

_____

What happened in the end: _____

_____

"All Stories Are Anansi's" by Harold Courlander
Enrichment: Making Plans

Suppose that, like Anansi, you want to own all the stories. Then, you, too, must capture Mmoboro, the hornets; Onini, the great python (a snake); and Osebo, the leopard, but you may not copy Anansi's methods. Will you use trickery or technology? Will you talk the animals into going with you? Unlike Anansi, you must catch all of the animals humanely, and they must be alive when you bring them to Nyame, the Sky God. Like Anansi's plans, yours should be fanciful. How will you do it?

DIRECTIONS: *Use this chart to map out your plans for capturing the hornets, the python, and the leopard. Describe your plan for each animal, or draw and label a diagram. Then, list the materials you will need.*

Mmoboro (the hornets): _____

_____

_____

_____

Materials: _____

_____

_____

Onini (the python): _____

_____

_____

_____

Materials: _____

_____

Osebo (the leopard): _____

_____

_____

_____

Materials: _____

_____

_____

"The People Could Fly" by Virginia Hamilton
"All Stories Are Anansi's" by Harold Courlander
Build Language Skills: Vocabulary

Idioms

An **idiomatic expression** is one in which the meaning of the expression is different from the meaning of the individual words that make up the expression. We are so accustomed to hearing idioms and idiomatic expressions that we may forget that they do not make sense if we take them literally. For example, in "The People Could Fly," Sarah is so worn out that she cannot sing to her baby. The narrator says, "She had no heart to croon to it." That does not mean that Sarah's heart has been removed. It means she does not have the will or the spirit to comfort the child.

A. DIRECTIONS: *Use the context to figure out the meaning of the underlined idiom in each sentence. Then, rewrite the sentence, using a* literal *expression for the idiom. A literal expression is one whose meaning does* not *differ from the meaning of the individual words that make it up.*

1. The story of the family who lost all their possessions in a flood <u>broke my heart</u>.

   _____

2. Tom took his teacher's advice <u>to heart</u> and immediately began studying harder.

   _____

Academic Vocabulary Practice

B. DIRECTIONS: *Indicate whether each statement is* true *or* false. *Then, explain your answer.*

1. When you *analyze* a problem, you express a generalization about it.

   T / F: _____ Explanation: _____

   _____

2. Suspense is not a *characteristic* of mystery stories.

   T / F: _____ Explanation: _____

   _____

3. An *aspect* of folk tales is the common character type.

   T / F: _____ Explanation: _____

   _____

4. A *detail* may be important or unimportant.

   T / F: _____ Explanation: _____

   _____

"The People Could Fly" by Virginia Hamilton
"All Stories Are Anansi's" by Harold Courlander
Build Language Skills: Grammar

Abbreviations

An **abbreviation** is a shortened form of a word or phrase. Most abbreviations end with a period, but many do not, and some may be written either with or without a period. Most dictionaries have entries for abbreviations, so look them up if you are not sure of the correct form. Note which abbreviations are written with periods, which ones are not, and which ones appear in capital letters in these lists:

Titles of persons: Mr. Ms. Mrs.

Days of the week: Sun. Mon. Tues. Wed. Thurs. Fri. Sat. Sun.

Months of the year: Jan. Feb. Mar. Apr. Aug. Sept. Oct. Nov. Dec.

Times of day: a.m. p.m.

Street designations: Ave. Blvd. Pl. St.

State postal abbreviations: AL AK AZ AR CA CO CT DE FL GA HI ID IL IN
IA KS KY LA ME MD MA MI MN MS MO MT NE NV NH NJ NM NY NC
ND OH OK OR PA RI SC SD TN TX UT VT VA WA WV WI WY

Organizations: NAACP UN YMCA

Units of measure: in. ft. yd. lb. qt. gal. *but* mm cm m mg g ml dl l

A. PRACTICE: *Rewrite each sentence below, and abbreviate the words in italics.*

1. James lives at 115 Elm *Street*, Pleasant Valley, *Nebraska*.

   _____

2. The gardener said that if your yard measures 50 *feet* (16.6 *yards*) by 40 *feet* (13.3 *yards*), you will need 2 *pounds* of fertilizer.

   _____

   _____

3. *Mister* Raymond works for the *United Nations*.

   _____

B. Writing Application: *Compose an e-mail message to a friend. Tell about something you have done recently. Use at least five abbreviations. If you are not sure of the correct form, look up the abbreviation in a dictionary.*

   _____

   _____

   _____

   _____

   _____

"All Stories Are Anansi's" by Harold Courlander
Selection Test A

Critical Reading *Identify the letter of the choice that best answers the question.*

____ 1. What do folk tales such as "All Stories Are Anansi's" often have in common?
   I.   plot elements
   II. settings
   III. character types
   IV. themes
   A. I, II, III
   B. II, III, IV
   C. I, II, IV
   D. I, III, IV

____ 2. At the beginning of "All Stories Are Anansi's," who owns all the stories?
   A. a spider
   B. a god
   C. a snake
   D. a human

____ 3. Based on "All Stories are Anansi's," what is important to the people who told this tale?
   A. spiders
   B. physical strength
   C. storytelling
   D. wealth

____ 4. With what tool does Anansi capture the hornets in "All Stories Are Anansi's"?
   A. a gourd
   B. a pit
   C. a bamboo pole
   D. a calabash

____ 5. In "All Stories Are Anansi's," after Anansi catches the hornets, he says,
   "Oh, yes, but you are really foolish people!"

   Why does he say that?
   A. because they dislike the rain
   B. because they trusted him
   C. because they do not sting him
   D. because they live in a tree

_____ 6. In "All Stories Are Anansi's," Anansi takes advantage of the python to capture him. Which character trait of the python does Anansi take advantage of?
A. his pride
B. his stupidity
C. his dishonesty
D. his physical weakness

_____ 7. In "All Stories Are Anansi's," when the leopard falls into the pit, why does Anansi say that he is "half-foolish"?
A. The leopard is smart enough to escape.
B. The leopard has fallen only halfway into the pit.
C. Anansi's plan to capture the leopard is only half finished.
D. Anansi does not know how to complete the job of capturing the leopard.

_____ 8. What do all the victims in "All Stories Are Anansi's" have in common?
A. greed
B. ambition
C. strength
D. foolishness

_____ 9. "All Stories Are Anansi's" is a trickster tale. Who is the trickster in the story?
A. Nyame
B. Anansi
C. the python
D. Osebo

_____ 10. In "All Stories Are Anansi's," how is Anansi's approach to all of his victims the same?
A. He overpowers them.
B. He hides from them.
C. He fools them.
D. He pays them.

_____ 11. How is Anansi different from all his victims in "All Stories Are Anansi's"?
A. He is smaller than they are.
B. He is weaker than they are.
C. He is smarter than they are.
D. He is poorer than they are.

____ 12. What lesson about life does one learn from "All Stories are Anansi's"?

   A. Do not be too quick to trust.

   B. Do not be afraid of the rain.

   C. Do not trust spiders.

   D. Do not fall into pits.

____ 13. What lesson about life is suggested by "All Stories Are Anansi's"?

   A. Intelligence is more important than strength.

   B. Spiders are more powerful than gods.

   C. Rulers are stronger than warriors.

   D. Animals are essentially foolish.

Vocabulary and Grammar

____ 14. In which sentence is the meaning of the word *yearned* expressed?

   A. Warriors and kings tried to own the stories, but they failed.

   B. Anansi wanted the stories so much he worked hard to get them.

   C. The python did not see that Anansi was going to trick him.

   D. The hornets hated water so much that they flew into the gourd.

____ 15. What does the abbreviation M.D. stand for in the following sentence?

   Rosa Gonzales, M.D., posted her hours on her office door.

   A. Maryland

   B. medical doctor

   C. miles per hour

   D. minutes after noon

Essay

16. Is Anansi in "All Stories Are Anansi's" an admirable character? That is, do you look up to him? Would you want to be like him? Why or why not? Present your opinion in an essay. Cite two details from the folk tale to support your main ideas.

17. Which of Anansi's victories in "All Stories Are Anansi's" did you find most impressive? Was it the way Anansi captured the hornets? The way he captured the python? The way he captured the leopard? In an essay, explain your choice. Cite two details from the selection to support your ideas.

Name _____ Date _____

"All Stories Are Anansi's" by Harold Courlander
Selection Test B

Critical Reading *Identify the letter of the choice that best completes the statement or answers the question.*

____ 1. Folk tales such as "All Stories Are Anansi's" are part of a tradition that includes which of the following kinds of literature?
  I.   fairy tales
  II. tall tales
  III. ghost stories
  IV. science fiction
  A. I only
  B. I and II only
  C. I, II, and III only
  D. I, II, III, and IV

____ 2. Which character owns all the stories when "All Stories Are Anansi's" begins?
  A. Anansi
  B. the Sky God
  C. the python
  D. Osebo

____ 3. What motivation does the major character have for his actions in "All Stories Are Anansi's"?
  A. Anansi wants to rule the forest.
  B. Anansi wants to impress the Sky God.
  C. Anansi wants to get rid of the hornets.
  D. Anansi wants to own all the stories.

____ 4. In "All Stories Are Anansi's," the price of owning all the stories is high. What does that tell you about the people who told this story?
  A. They valued storytelling.
  B. They valued trickery.
  C. They valued wealth.
  D. They valued spiders.

____ 5. In "All Stories Are Anansi's," Anansi approaches the python by
  A. flattering him.
  B. insulting him.
  C. questioning him.
  D. challenging him.

____ 6. In "All Stories Are Anansi's," how is Anansi's treatment of the leopard different from his treatment of his other victims?
  A. He calls him foolish.
  B. He talks to him.
  C. He tricks him.
  D. He kills him.

Name _____ Date _____

_____ 7. In "All Stories Are Anansi's," what is the same about Anansi's approach to all of his victims?
   A. He bribes them.
   B. He kills them.
   C. He outsmarts them.
   D. He kidnaps them.

_____ 8. Which attribute does Anansi use to capture all his victims?
   A. his ability to spin webs
   B. his ability to avoid traps
   C. his ability to talk to the Sky God
   D. his ability to use his intelligence

_____ 9. Folk tales often show one character taking advantage of other characters. Which character trait of his victims does Anansi take advantage of in "All Stories Are Anansi's"?
   A. their intelligence
   B. their naivete
   C. their greed
   D. their anger

_____ 10. Which two traits are contrasted in "All Stories Are Anansi's"?
   A. strength and weakness
   B. good and evil
   C. intelligence and foolishness
   D. ambition and laziness

_____ 11. What lesson about life is taught in "All Stories Are Anansi's"?
   A. Ambition will make you wealthy.
   B. Storytelling can be dangerous.
   C. Warriors may be defeated.
   D. Trust given quickly is foolish.

_____ 12. Which word best describes Anansi's attitude toward the other animals?
   A. respect
   B. contempt
   C. appreciation
   D. puzzlement

_____ 13. Why is Anansi able to do what warriors and chiefs failed to do?
   A. He uses thought instead of weapons.
   B. He is more powerful than the warriors.
   C. He uses words instead of money.
   D. He uses the language of animals.

____ 14. What contrast between Anansi and his victims in "All Stories Are Anansi's" makes the victims unable to believe that Anansi poses a danger to them?
A. They are so much bigger than he is.
B. They are so much richer than he is.
C. They are so much smarter than he is.
D. They are so much prouder than he is.

Vocabulary and Grammar

____ 15. In which sentence does the word *gourd* make sense?
A. The thirsty explorer drank from a *gourd*.
B. We bandaged our wounds with a *gourd*.
C. The *gourd* escaped and ran to the bushes.
D. The scientist made notes with a *gourd*.

____ 16. In which sentence is the meaning of the word *acknowledge* expressed?
A. A representative of the company questioned whether we had paid our bill.
B. Millions of people vote in every national election in the United States.
C. The writer gives credit for the ideas he uses from other sources.
D. Our animals are never let out to roam around the neighborhood.

____ 17. Which of the following abbreviations is correct?
A. cm. for *centimeter*
B. in for *inch*
C. Penn for *Pennsylvania*
D. ml for *milliliter*

____ 18. Which of the following abbreviations is correct?
A. M.S. for *Mississippi*
B. Miss. for *Miss*
C. M.S. for *master of science*
D. Ms. for *Mister*

Essay

19. Anansi pays a hugh price to gain possession of all the tales and all the stories, but "All Stories Are Anansi's" never explains why Anansi wants those tales and stories in the first place. What do you think motivates Anansi? Does he just want to do something that the wealthiest and most powerful families have failed to do? Does he have some other motive? In an essay, express your ideas. Cite a detail from the story to support your opinion.

20. A folk tale can tell a reader a great deal about the people who traditionally told the tale. In an essay, tell what "All Stories Are Anansi's" tells you about the people who told that tale. What does it tell you about their environment? What does it tell you that they valued? What lessons were they likely to pass on to their children? Cite three details from the tale to support your ideas.

"The Fox Outwits the Crow" by William Cleary
"The Fox and the Crow" by Aesop
Vocabulary Warm-up Word Lists

Study these words from "The Fox Outwits the Crow" and "The Fox and the Crow." Then, complete the activities that follow.

Word List A

curves [KERVZ] *n.* lines or shapes that bend like parts of a circle
The car hugged the road as it traveled around the mountain <u>curves</u>.

figure [FIG yoor] *n.* a person's shape
The designer's clothes looked great on the model's perfect <u>figure</u>.

fondly [FAHND lee] *adv.* in a way that shows you like someone or something very much
Greta smiled <u>fondly</u> at grandfather from across the table.

snatch [SNACH] *v.* to take or grab something quickly
I saw two thieves <u>snatch</u> apples from the fruit vendor's cart.

trust [TRUST] *v.* to believe that someone is honest and dependable
The mechanic was the one person Jack could <u>trust</u> to fix his car.

whiff [WIF] *n.* a faint smell in the air
We smelled a <u>whiff</u> of smoke coming from the car engine.

Word List B

advice [ad VYS] *n.* an opinion about what someone should do
Shelly followed her friends' <u>advice</u> to stay home until she was well.

exchange [iks CHAYNJ] *v.* to give one thing for another
Carter wanted to <u>exchange</u> his new watch for a dirt bike.

flattery [FLAT er ee] *n.* nice things you say to someone, but you do not mean
<u>Flattery</u> is the least sincere form of admiration.

glamorous [GLAM er uhs] *adj.* attractive and exciting
The famous actress lived a <u>glamorous</u> lifestyle.

malice [MAL is] *n.* the desire to harm or upset someone
The man accused his innocent neighbor with intentional <u>malice</u>.

moral [MAWR uhl] *n.* the lesson taught by a story
The <u>moral</u> of "The Tortoise and the Hare" is "slow and steady wins the race."

Name _____ Date _____

"The Fox Outwits the Crow" by William Cleary
"The Fox and the Crow" by Aesop
Vocabulary Warm-up Exercises

Exercise A *Fill in each blank in the paragraph below with an appropriate word from Word List A. Use each word only once.*

The firefighters could smell a [1] _____ of smoke as the fire truck sped around the mountainous [2] _____. Just as the truck reached the burning cabin, a woman's [3] _____ emerged from the billowing smoke. She was carrying a small child. One firefighter [4] _____ two oxygen masks out of the truck and rushed toward the woman. He gave one mask to the woman and put other one over the child's face. When paramedics arrived, the woman handed them her child, knowing she could [5] _____ them to make sure he was all right. With a sigh of relief, she looked [6] _____ at the firefighters who had helped to ensure their safety.

Exercise B *Write a complete sentence to answer each question. Use a word from Word List B to replace each underlined word without changing the meaning.*

Example: How do you feel about <u>meaningless compliments</u>?
    I think <u>flattery</u> is insulting.

1. What is the most <u>exciting</u> thing you have ever done?
   _____

2. Why would you never act out of <u>meanness</u> toward a friend?
   _____

3. On what occasion do you <u>trade</u> cards or gifts?
   _____

4. Why do people like stories with a <u>lesson</u>?
   _____

5. What <u>opinion</u> would you give someone who is paying too much for an item?
   _____

"The Fox Outwits the Crow" by William Cleary
"The Fox and the Crow" by Aesop
Reading Warm-up A

Read the following passage. Pay special attention to the underlined words. Then, read it again, and complete the activities. Use a separate sheet of paper for your written answers.

On her sixteenth birthday, Mira went into the garden wearing the new gown her mother <u>fondly</u> had made for her. Every seam was lovingly stitched so that the fabric perfectly fitted the <u>curves</u> of her body. "Today," she thought dreamily, "I am the prettiest girl in the village."

"That is true," said a musical voice that tickled her ear.

Mira turned to see the <u>figure</u> of a man wearing clothes of purple satin and a peacock-feathered hat. He held a jeweled mirror, and he stared at his own reflection. Mira smelled a <u>whiff</u> of his perfume and sneezed.

"Bless you!" said the figure, never taking his eyes from the mirror.

"Who are you?" asked Mira. "Tell me what is true."

"My name is Vanity," he answered silkily, his eyes still on the mirror, "and you *are* the prettiest girl in the village." With a crook of his finger, he beckoned Mira toward the mirror.

Mira saw a reflection of herself in her new gown. Now, however, the gown was made of gold, and pearls dangled from her earlobes. Her skin glowed like a fresh peach. Her hair shimmered in the sun. She was beautiful!

"Is this a true image of me?" she asked.

"<u>Trust</u> me, it is," said Vanity, "and I tell no lies."

Mira <u>snatched</u> the mirror from Vanity's grasp and stared long at her image. When she looked up, he was gone, but she still held the mirror.

From that day forward, Mira had eyes only for the image in the mirror. She saw herself as no one else ever saw her, and she saw no one else at all. Then one day, the mirror cracked and she was old.

Sadly she saw the truth at last: Vanity had robbed her of her true self, leaving her empty. Vanity had lied.

1. Circle the word that is a synonym for <u>fondly</u>. Use *fondly* in a sentence.

2. Underline the words that tell what <u>curves</u> the fabric fitted. Write the meaning of *curves*.

3. Circle the words that tell what kind of <u>figure</u> Mira saw. Rewrite the sentence using a synonym for *figure*.

4. Underline the words that tell what Mira caught a <u>whiff</u> of. Write about something else you might get a *whiff* of.

5. Circle the word that tells who Mira was asked to <u>trust</u>. Name someone you *trust* and tell why.

6. Circle the word that tells what Mira <u>snatched</u>. Give a synonym for *snatched* and use it in a sentence.

"The Fox Outwits the Crow" by William Cleary
"The Fox and the Crow" by Aesop
Reading Warm-up B

Read the following passage. Pay special attention to the underlined words. Then, read it again, and complete the activities. Use a separate sheet of paper for your written answers.

One crow for sorrow, Two crows for mirth . . .

So begins an old counting rhyme that reflects the different ways in which the crow is viewed in folklore. The crow is a familiar figure. Although it's not as <u>glamorous</u> as many tropical birds, the crow has been both feared and admired since ancient times.

In nature, the crow belongs to a family of birds that includes the raven and the magpie. They are *carrion* birds, meaning they eat dead flesh. Crows, in fact, will eat anything: eggs, fish, acorns, berries, grains, insects. They are good at stealing food, too. Crows will band together to steal another animal's meal; however, they will rarely steal from each other. Within their group, they generously share and <u>exchange</u> bits of food.

In folklore the crow is often an omen of death. The bird's color and carrion diet probably contribute to this association. Crows are sometimes portrayed as creatures of <u>malice</u>, committing acts of evil intent. This is the dark side of the "trickster" crow. In one fable, however, the table is turned. A vain crow is tricked by false words of <u>flattery</u>. The <u>moral</u> of the tale holds this lesson for the crow: *as you trick, so will you be tricked.*

In some cultures, the crow represents laughter and the spirit of mischief. It is a still a trickster, but its tricks benefit humankind. Native Americans admire the crow's intelligence and ability to mimic speech. Their stories often cast the crow as a messenger for humans seeking <u>advice</u> from spirits.

Bird of sorrow, bird of mirth: the crow is a complex creature both in nature and native lore.

1. Circle the words that tell what the crow is not as <u>glamorous</u> as. Describe something or someone that you think of as *glamorous*.

2. Underline the words that tell what crows sometimes <u>exchange</u>. Write the meaning of *exchange*.

3. Underline the words that mean the same as <u>malice</u>. Write a sentence using the word *malice*.

4. Circle the words that mean the same as <u>flattery</u>. Describe a situation in which someone might use *flattery*.

5. Circle the word that is a synonym for <u>moral</u>. Tell the *moral* of a familiar story and what it means to you.

6. Circle the words that tell from whom humans seek <u>advice</u> in Native American lore. Use *advice* in a sentence.

Name _____ Date _____

"The Fox Outwits the Crow" by William Cleary
"The Fox and the Crow" by Aesop
Literary Analysis: Comparing Tone

The **tone** of a literary work is the writer's attitude toward his or her subject and characters. The tone can often be described by a single adjective, such as *formal, playful,* or *respectful.* Factors that contribute to the tone include word choice, details, sentence structure, rhythm, and rhyme.

The poem "The Fox Outwits the Crow" and the fable "The Fox and the Crow" have similar characters, settings, and plots, but the authors who wrote them have different attitudes toward their subject. To determine the tone of each selection, notice the words and phrases that the authors use to express their ideas.

DIRECTIONS: *Compare the tone of the two selections about the fox and the crow by completing this chart. Choose one adjective to describe each passage. Use* serious, formal, informal, *or* playful. *Then, answer the question that follows.*

"The Fox Outwits the Crow"	Adjective	"The Fox and the Crow"	Adjective
1. One day a young Crow snatched a fat piece of cheese.		A Fox once saw a Crow fly off with a piece of cheese in its beak.	
2. A Fox . . . got a whiff of the cheese, / The best of his favorite hors d'oeuvres		"That's for me, as I am a Fox," said master Reynard.	
3. Hey, you glamorous thing, / Does your voice match your beautiful curves?		"I feel sure your voice must surpass that of other birds, just as your figure does."	
4. She opened her mouth—and the cheese tumbled out, /		The moment she opened her mouth the . . . cheese fell to the ground . . .	
5. Which the Fox gobbled up full of malice		only to be snapped up by Master Fox.	
6. While he chuckled to think how that dim-witted Crow		"That will do," said he. "That was all I wanted."	
7. Could believe she was MARIA CALLAS		"In exchange for your cheese I will give you . . . advice for the future—"	

8. What is each author's attitude toward his subject and his characters?

_____

Name _____ Date _____

Vocabulary Builder

Word List

whiff	hors d'oeuvres	malice	glossy	surpass	flatterers

A. DIRECTIONS: *Circle* T *if the statement is true and* F *if the statement is false. Then, explain your answer.*

1. A true bloodhound can follow someone's trail after getting only a *whiff* of the person's odor.

   T / F _____

2. *Flatterers* are honest and sincere.

   T / F _____

3. Something that is *glossy* has a rough finish.

   T / F _____

4. Most people would feel *malice* toward someone who has harmed them.

   T / F _____

5. *Hors d'oeuvres* are served after the main course.

   T / F _____

6. For a person to *surpass* expectations, he or she must do better than expected.

   T / F _____

B. DIRECTIONS: *For each pair of words in CAPITAL LETTERS, write the letter of the pair of words that best expresses a similar relationship.*

____ 1. OUTDO : SURPASS ::
    A. lose : win
    B. talk : remember
    C. work : play
    D. throw : toss

____ 2. WHIFF : SCENT ::
    A. sight : hearing
    B. good : bad
    C. love : adoration
    D. eyes : nose

____ 3. MALICE : GOODWILL ::
    A. stroll : walk
    B. painter : artist
    C. large : humongous
    D. blame : praise

Name _____ Date _____

"The Fox Outwits the Crow" by William Cleary

"The Fox and the Crow" by Aesop

Support for Writing to Compare Reactions to Tone

Use this graphic organizer to take notes for an essay that compares your reaction to the author's tone in "The Fox Outwits the Crow" with your reaction to the author's tone in "The Fox and the Crow."

"The Fox Outwits the Crow"   **"The Fox and the Crow"**

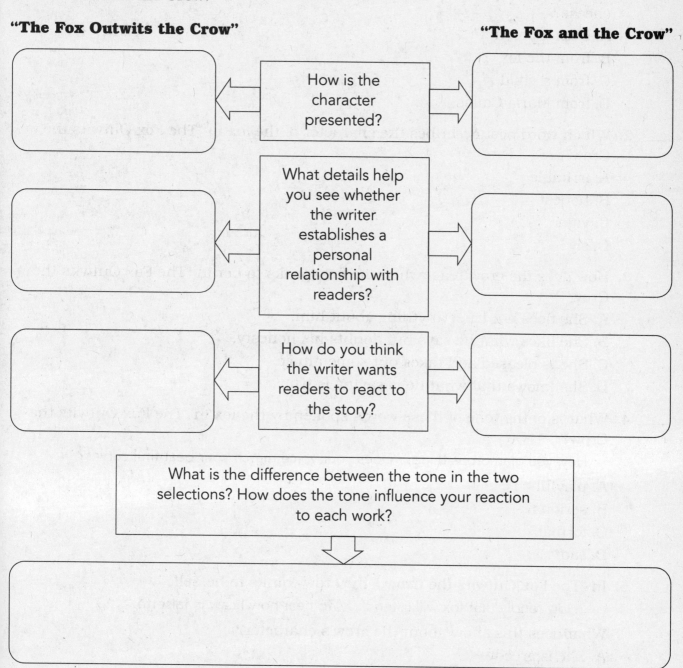

Now, use your notes to write an essay in which you compare your reaction to the tone of "The Fox Outwits the Crow" with your reaction to the tone of "The Fox and the Crow."

Name _____ Date _____

"The Fox Outwits the Crow" by William Cleary
"The Fox and the Crow" by Aesop
Selection Test A

Critical Reading *Identify the letter of the choice that best answers the question.*

____ 1. In the poem "The Fox Outwits the Crow," where does the crow get the piece of cheese?
A. from a porch
B. from the fox
C. from a child
D. from Maria Callas

____ 2. Which word best describes the character of the fox in "The Fox Outwits the Crow"?
A. irritable
B. honest
C. vain
D. sly

____ 3. How does the crow react when the fox speaks to her in "The Fox Outwits the Crow"?
A. She does not trust anything about him.
B. She likes what he says but doubts his honesty.
C. She is pleased and takes out some music.
D. She knows that what he is saying is true.

____ 4. What is of the tone of these words spoken by the fox in "The Fox Outwits the Crow"?

Hey, you glamorous thing, / Does your voice match your beautiful curves?

A. playful
B. serious
C. formal
D. sad

____ 5. In "The Fox Outwits the Crow," the crow thinks to herself,

"How fondly that fox will listen . . . / To hear how I caw in falsetto."

What does this show about the crow's character?
A. She is greedy.
B. She is angry.
C. She is happy.
D. She is proud.

Unit 6 Resources: Themes in the Oral Tradition

____ 6. In "The Fox and the Crow," why does the Fox want the Crow to sing?
   A. so that he may sing with her
   B. so that he can make fun of her voice
   C. so that she will drop the piece of cheese she has
   D. so that she can serenade him with beautiful music

____ 7. What word best describes the character of the Crow in "The Fox and the Crow"?
   A. sly
   B. vain
   C. honest
   D. irritable

____ 8. What is the tone of these words spoken by the Fox in "The Fox and the Crow"?
   "I feel sure your voice must surpass that of other birds, just as your figure does."
   A. sad
   B. formal
   C. angry
   D. funny

____ 9. Which statement best expresses the moral of "The Fox and the Crow"?
   A. Nothing lasts forever.
   B. Value your friends.
   C. Do not trust flattery.
   D. Friends may turn against you.

____ 10. How might the tone of a literary work such as "The Fox and the Crow" or "The Fox Outwits the Crow" be described?
   A. It is the subject of the work.
   B. It is the writer's attitude.
   C. It is the characters' attitude.
   D. It is the message of the work.

____ 11. How does the tone of "The Fox and the Crow" compare with the tone of "The Fox Outwits the Crow"?
   A. The tone of "The Fox and the Crow" is more serious.
   B. The tone of "The Fox and the Crow" is more comical.
   C. The tone of "The Fox and the Crow" is more playful.
   D. The tone of "The Fox and the Crow" is more informal.

___ 12. How does the tone of "The Fox Outwits the Crow" compare with the tone of "The Fox and the Crow"?

    A. The tone of "The Fox Outwits the Crow" is more serious.

    B. The tone of "The Fox Outwits the Crow" is more suspenseful.

    C. The tone of "The Fox Outwits the Crow" is more playful.

    D. The tone of "The Fox Outwits the Crow" is more formal.

Vocabulary

___ 13. Where would you most likely find *hors d'oeuvres*?

    A. at a concert

    B. at school

    C. on a train

    D. at a party

___ 14. What item is most likely to be described as *glossy*?

    A. a rough stone

    B. a waxed floor

    C. a wool sweater

    D. an old frying pan

___ 15. In which sentence is the meaning of *surpass* expressed?

    A. In their slyness, foxes are superior to all other animals.

    B. If you are fooled by the fox, you will not be alone.

    C. Crows are known to have unpleasant voices.

    D. Crows are not well-known for their vanity.

Essay

16. The crow is a character in many literary works. In an essay, compare and contrast the Crow in the fable "The Fox and the Crow" with the crow in the poem "The Fox Outwits the Crow." What does each crow do? What does each crow learn?

17. The fox is a common character in fables and other stories. In an essay, compare and contrast the Fox in the fable "The Fox and the Crow" with the fox in the poem "The Fox Outwits the Crow." What does each fox do? What tone does each fox's words contribute to the selection?

Name _____ Date _____

"The Fox Outwits the Crow" by William Cleary
"The Fox and the Crow" by Aesop
Selection Test B

Critical Reading *Identify the letter of the choice that best completes the statement or answers the question.*

____ 1. In "The Fox Outwits the Crow," the crow gets a piece of cheese from
   A. the back yard of a stone house.
   B. the front yard of a brick house.
   C. the porch of a stone house.
   D. the attic of a brick house.

____ 2. In "The Fox Outwits the Crow," the crow takes the cheese to the top of a tree in order to
   A. share it with other birds.
   B. show off to the forest what she has.
   C. enjoy it by herself.
   D. get away from the fox.

____ 3. What is the tone of these words spoken by the fox in "The Fox Outwits the Crow"?
   "Hey, you glamorous thing, / Does your voice match your beautiful curves?"
   A. playful
   B. serious
   C. formal
   D. arrogant

____ 4. In "The Fox Outwits the Crow," what quality of the crow's character is evident as she thinks these thoughts?
   "How fondly that fox will listen, . . . / To hear how I caw in falsetto."
   A. greed
   B. anger
   C. happiness
   D. pride

____ 5. The character of the fox in "The Fox Outwits the Crow" could best be described as
   A. irritable.
   B. honest.
   C. vain.
   D. sly.

____ 6. In "The Fox Outwits the Crow," the crow's reaction to the fox shows that the crow
   A. is pleased by the fox's flattery.
   B. is suspicious of the fox's flattery.
   C. is sure of the fox's insincerity.
   D. is angered by the fox's insincerity.

_____ 7. In "The Fox and the Crow," why does the Fox says that he wants to hear the Crow sing?
  A. He wants to hear beautiful music.
  B. He wants to make fun of the Crow's voice.
  C. He wants to sing with the Crow.
  D. He wants to get the cheese the Crow has.

_____ 8. How would the Fox's tone best be described in this line from "The Fox and the Crow"?
  "I feel sure your voice must surpass that of other birds, just as your figure does."
  A. informal
  B. formal
  C. angry
  D. amusing

_____ 9. Which word best describes the character of the Crow in "The Fox and the Crow"?
  A. sly
  B. vain
  C. honest
  D. irritable

_____ 10. Which statement best describes the moral of "The Fox and the Crow"?
  A. Birds of a feather flock together.
  B. The end justifies the means.
  C. Compliments may be used to deceive.
  D. You can kill two birds with one stone.

_____ 11. In "The Fox and the Crow," why does Aesop advise the reader not to trust flatterers?
  A. Flatterers may have hidden motives.
  B. Flatterers are liars.
  C. Flatterers only want attention.
  D. Flatterers are too kind to tell the truth.

_____ 12. In a literary work such as "The Fox and the Crow" or "The Fox Outwits the Crow," the tone may be described as the writer's
  A. attitude.
  B. words.
  C. characters.
  D. adjectives.

_____ 13. Compared with the tone of "The Fox Outwits the Crow," the tone of "The Fox and the Crow" is more
  A. serious.
  B. comical.
  C. playful.
  D. informal.

____ 14. Compared with the tone of "The Fox and the Crow," the tone of "The Fox Outwits the Crow" is more
   A. serious.
   B. distant.
   C. playful.
   D. formal.

Vocabulary

____ 15. In what situation would you most likely encounter *hors d'oeuvres*?
   A. at a museum
   B. at a concert
   C. on a boat
   D. at a reception

____ 16. Which item is most likely to be *glossy*?
   A. a sweater
   B. a magazine
   C. a book
   D. a piece of cheese

____ 17. People who *surpass* something are most likely to be considered
   A. achievers.
   B. flatterers.
   C. failures.
   D. athletes.

Essay

18. The crow is a character in many literary works. In an essay, compare and contrast the Crow in "The Fox and the Crow" with the crow in "The Fox Outwits the Crow." Describe how they are different and how they are alike. Tell what each crow does and what each crow learns. Is one crow's attitude more extreme than the other? Explain your answer.

19. A reader can discover the tone of a literary work by analyzing descriptive details, word choice, and sentence structure. In an essay, compare and contrast the tone of "The Fox and the Crow" with that of "The Fox Outwits the Crow." Consider these elements: How do the characters speak? What details are included? Finally, answer these questions: How do you think the writer wants you to react to the work? How does the tone of each selection influence your attitude toward the work? Explain your answer.

Name _____ Date _____

Research: Research Report

Prewriting: Choosing a Topic

To choose the right topic to research, answer the following questions according to your own interests.

Question:	Answer:
What broad subject interests you?	
What specific categories of that subject do you find appealing?	
What people in history would you like to understand better?	
What current event would you like to understand better?	

Drafting: Making an Outline

Review your prewriting notes and group them by category; then, complete the following outline to organize your supporting details.

Your Thesis Statement:

I. _____

  A. _____

  B. _____

II. _____

  A. _____

  B. _____

III. _____

  A. _____

  B. _____

Name _____ Date _____

Research Report: Integrating Grammar Skills

Revising for the Correct Case of Pronouns

Case is the relationship between a pronoun's form and its role in a sentence. Pronouns can be one of three cases: nominative, objective, or possessive.

Case	Pronouns	Role in Sentence	Example
Nominative	I, we you he, she, it, they	subject of a verb predicate pronoun (after a linking verb)	*We* walked to school. The best students were Jan and *I.*
Objective	me, us you him, her, it, them	direct object indirect object object of a preposition	The teacher helped *us.* Get *him* a book. Give that book to *them.*
Possessive	my, mine; our, ours your, yours his; her, hers; its; their, theirs	to show ownership	Jo is at *her* locker. That locker is *yours.*

Identifying the Correct Case of Pronouns

A. DIRECTIONS: *Circle the pronoun that correctly completes each sentence.*

1. Jackie and (them, they) are on the softball team
2. The coach taught Sonya and (she, her) a new pitch.
3. Were you throwing the ball to Tanya or (I, me)?
4. The close game really excited Sally and (we, us).

Fixing the Incorrect Case of Pronouns

B. DIRECTIONS: *On the lines provided, rewrite these sentences so that they use the correct pronouns. If a sentence is correct as presented, write* correct.

1. Wendell, Terry, and me like to play basketball.

_____

2. Terry's brother taught Wendell and I some good moves.

_____

3. Often Wendell's older brother joins Wendell and us in a game.

_____

4. Him and Terry's brother have been playing together for years.

_____

Spelling Workshop—Unit 6
Greek Roots and Word Families

Words built around the same root make up a **word family.** Often, these roots are spelled in only one or two ways. This is true of the Greek roots *chron* (meaning "time"), *phon* (meaning "sound"), and *aster* or *astro* (meaning "star"). To spell words with these roots correctly, focus on the surrounding parts of the word as well as on the spelling of the root.

Word List

asterisk	astronomy	chronological	phonics	symphony
astronaut	chronic	disaster	saxophone	synchronize

A. DIRECTIONS: *Write the word from the Word List that matches each clue.*

1. many instruments playing the same music _____

2. either alphabetical or _____ order _____

3. a way of learning how to pronounce sounds _____

4. catastrophe _____

5. study of the stars and planets _____

6. continuing for a long time _____

7. make several things happen at the same time _____

8. member of a spaceship crew _____

9. a musical instrument _____

10. marked items on a list with a(n) _____ _____

B. DIRECTIONS: *For each item below, choose three list words with the same root. Then, write two related sentences using the words you chose.*

1. words I chose: _____

_____

_____

2. words I chose: _____

_____

_____

3. words I chose: _____

_____

_____

Name _____ Date _____

Conducting an Interview

After choosing a person to interview, fill out the following chart to complete the interview and gather the information you need.

Topic of interview: _____

What kind of information are you trying to get during the interview?
What research have you done to prepare for the interview?
What questions do you plan to ask?
What follow-up questions might there be?

For Further Reading—Unit 6

DIRECTIONS: *Think about the books you have read. Then, on a separate sheet of paper, answer the discussion questions and take notes for your literary circle.*

Destiny by Vicki Grove

Discussion Miss Valentino says art expresses passionate dreams, Destiny's mother says art should go with your sofa, and Mrs. Peck says art tells about the civilization that created it. How does each statement tell something about the character who said it?

Connections: Literature Circle Destiny retells the story of Pandora and says that evil took root in the world because of Pandora's "stupid nosiness." What had Pandora done? Why does it seem to mean a lot to Destiny that "hope" is the one thing left in Pandora's jar?

Myths and Legends From Ancient Greece and Around the World—Prentice Hall Anthology

Discussion In "The Judgment of Paris," what does the behavior of Minerva, Juno, and Venus show about how the Greeks viewed their gods and goddesses?

Connections: Literature Circle In "How Grandmother Spider Named the Clans," who established the clans and their territories? What message might clan members find in this story? Explain.

The Gawgon and the Boy by Lloyd Alexander

Discussion: David's opinion of Aunt Annie changes as he gets to know her. Discuss the reasons that David's opinion of Aunt Annie changes.

Connections: Literary Circles Think about people you know who are very different than you first thought they were. Then speculate about what people first think about you that is incorrect. Why do you think that we form judgments without knowing people?

The Prince and the Pauper by Mark Twain

Discussion Think about why Edward and Tom decide to switch clothes. Why does Tom want to dress like a prince? Why does Ed want to dress like a pauper?

Connections: Literature Circle Edward has experienced the life that Tom had as one of the ordinary people. Why do you think Edward's experiences might make him a better king after he is returned to his rightful place in the palace? Explain your reasons.

Unit 6: Themes in the Oral Tradition
Part 2 Benchmark Test 12

MULTIPLE CHOICE

Reading Skill: Compare and Contrast

1. Which choice best describes a Venn diagram?
   A. two or more circles in a straight line with no points overlapping
   B. two or more circles that overlap one another
   C. two or more circles of exactly the same size right on top of one another
   D. two or more circles having the same center but of increasingly larger size

2. If you are comparing and contrasting two things, how many circles would you need in your Venn diagram?
   A. two
   B. three
   C. four
   D. five

Read the selection. Then, answer the questions that follow.

During the Middle Ages, knights wore armor to protect themselves in battle. The armor helped prevent serious injury and death. Arrows, swords, lances, clubs, and spears were the main weapons. A suit of armor was thick and awkward, like an astronaut's spacesuit. It usually included metal plates to protect the body, chain mail worn underneath, and a metal helmet with a hinged visor that could be raised and lowered over the eyes. The chain mail, which was made of thousands of small linked metal rings, moved more easily with the body than the metal plates. It was often worn alone in areas of frequent movement, such as the neck and wrists. Even with chain mail, a suit of armor still made movement very difficult. It was also extremely heavy—the chain mail alone often weighed over fifty pounds.

3. Which of the following comparisons help you "picture" how the knight looked?
   A. It compares the armor to arrows, swords, and other weapons.
   B. It compares a suit of armor to an astronaut's spacesuit.
   C. It compares the metal plates of armor to the helmet worn on the head.
   D. It compares the thickness of the armor to the weight of the chain mail.

4. If you were using a Venn diagram to help you compare and contrast chain mail and the metal plates in a suit of armor, which of these details would you list in the similarities space?
   A. made of metal rings
   B. moves easily with the body
   C. often worn on the neck
   D. very heavy

5. Which of these more familiar modern items would be most similar armor?
   A. a pair of blue jeans
   B. a helicopter
   C. a bulletproof vest
   D. a computer program

6. Which of these modern jobs would be most similar to a knight in the Middle Ages?
   A. a soldier
   B. a TV newscaster
   C. a bank teller
   D. a big-city mayor

Name _____ Date _____

Read this brief editorial from a local newspaper. Then, answer the questions that follow.

Easing the Village Traffic Problem

There is no question that weekend traffic has become a problem in our village. With the beginning of spring, weekend visitors arrive to enjoy the shops and gardens. In summer, the problem only gets worse, with vacationing tourists bringing congestion not only on weekends but also on weekdays. Fall means the foliage season, with bus tours as well as private cars, and no sooner is that done than Christmas shopping is upon us. In January and February, there is a brief lull in the number of visitors. Clearly, our narrow village roads were not built to accommodate so much traffic. What can we do to solve the problem? Many have suggested that city planners seek help from the state to build a new road that would bypass the center of town and ease the traffic burden there. However, this idea seems unwise to us. A much better idea, in our opinion, is to create two free parking lots outside town and advise tourists to park in them. We should then invest in a small fleet of shuttle buses that would take the tourists downtown and back.

7. What is the main purpose of an editorial?
   A. to describe
   B. to explain
   C. to persuade
   D. to tell a story

8. Which of these details support the idea that traffic congestion is a problem?
   A. Weekend visitors crowd into town to enjoy the shops and gardens.
   B. In January and February, there is a brief lull in the number of visitors.
   C. Tax dollars from the state are in short supply these days.
   D. The local economy relies heavily on the tourist business.

9. What solution does the editorial present for solving the problem of traffic congestion?
   A. creating a parking lot or buying shuttle buses
   B. building a new bypass road or creating parking lots with shuttle buses
   C. building a new bypass road or getting the state to build one
   D. creating parking lots with shuttle buses or stopping the tourist business

10. What is compared in the second and third sentences of the editorial?
   A. They compare traffic in the village with traffic in other places.
   B. They compare traffic from tourists with local traffic.
   C. They compare traffic in spring with traffic in summer.
   D. They compare warm weather in spring with hot weather in summer.

Literary Analysis: Folk Tales

11. Which of the following is the best definition of a folk tale?
   A. a story that features human characters who display traits like those of animals
   B. a story that features an ordinary hero or heroine who performs extraordinary deeds
   C. a story that is designed to teach a lesson that does not include any animal characters
   D. a story composed orally and passed down by word of mouth before being written down

12. Which of the following statements is true of folk tales?
   A. Folk tales from different cultures usually have different plot elements.
   B. Folk tales from different cultures usually have different character types.
   C. Folk tales often present a clear separation between good and evil.
   D. Most folk tales are not part of the oral tradition.

13. Which of the following does a textbook usually provide to help you understand the cultural context of a folk tale?
   A. a character description and short summary of the events in the folk tale
   B. a paragraph of background information that introduces the folk tale
   C. a list of vocabulary words that appear in the folk tale
   D. questions that have you compare and contrast characters in the folk tale

Read this folk tale from Ethiopia. Then, answer the questions that follow.

Long ago, a young man named Arha found work in Addis Ababa as the servant of a rich man named Haptom Hasei. One day, the rich man made a bet that no one could sleep on Mount Intotto without a fire to stay warm. He offered ten acres of land to anyone who could do it. Deciding to take up the bet, Arha sought advice from a wise old man. The old man said, "I will build a fire far from the mountain but close enough for you to see. Seeing the fire, you can imagine the warmth." So that is what Arha did and he managed to endure the whole night. The next day, however, Haptom Hasei refused to honor the bet since, he argued, a fire had been built. Arha took the matter to a judge, who ruled in favor of the rich man. That night, a friend of the wise man, invited Haptom Hasei and the judge to dinner. The guests could smell the wonderful food, but it was never brought out for them to eat. When they complained, the friend got them to agree that food smelled from a distance was not the same as food they could eat. The judge realized this error, and reversed his ruling so that Arha won his bet.

14. What lesson does this Ethiopian folk tale teach about the agreements people make?
   A. Always have at least one witness to any agreement you make.
   B. Be careful to follow all agreements precisely and to pay attention to their wording.
   C. A rich person is more likely to break an agreement than a poor person is.
   D. People should be true to the spirit of an agreement and not escape on a technicality.

15. Which of the following conclusions can you draw about the cultural context of the folk tale?
   A. Everyone in Ethiopia used to live in the city of Addis Ababa.
   B. In Ethiopia, farmers were more prosperous than merchants.
   C. Ethiopians used tribal elders, not judges, to rule on disagreements.
   D. Rural Ethiopians often took advice from wise men in their tribes.

16. Which of the following is an important difference between Addis Ababa and Mount Intotto?
   A. Addis Ababa is a city.
   B. Addis Ababa has more poor people.
   C. Mount Intotto is colder at night.
   D. Mount Intotto is far from Addis Ababa.

17. If you were using a Venn diagram to compare and contrast the characters of Arha and Haptom Hasei, where would you put the word *rich*?

    A. on the part of the Venn diagram that applies to Haptom Hasei only

    B. on the part of the Venn diagram that applies to both Arha and Haptom Hasei

    C. on the part of the Venn diagram that applies to Arha only

    D. on the part of the Venn diagram that applies to neither Arha nor Haptom Hasei

Literary Analysis: Tone

18. What does the tone of a literary work generally express?

    A. the attitude of the writer

    B. the attitude of the reader

    C. the mood of a character

    D. the atmosphere of a setting

19. Which of the following choices best describes the tone of this sentence?

    The remarkable founders of our nation bravely risked their lives and reputations to fight for the dream of American independence.

    A. angry

    B. humorous

    C. sad

    D. admiring

20. Compare and contrast the tones of these two sentences:

    The store teemed with Christmas spirit as jolly shoppers made last-minute purchases.

    The store teemed with shoppers shoving their way through their last-minute purchases.

    A. The tone of the first sentence is calm and unemotional while the tone of the second sentence is angry.

    B. The tone of the first sentence is warm and pleasant while the tone of the second sentence is irritated.

    C. The tone of the first sentence is happy and carefree while the tone of the second sentence is sad.

    D. The tone of the first sentence is joyful while the tone of the second sentence is calm and unemotional.

Vocabulary: Idioms

21. Which of the following choices gives the best defines an idiom?

    A. a wise saying that gives guidance in human behavior

    B. a phrase that takes the place of a noun and can be used as a subject or an object

    C. an expression passed down orally for generations before being written down

    D. an expression that has a meaning different from the words that make it up

22. Which of the following is an idiom?

    The twin sisters always welcome visitors and told me to drop by whenever I could.

    A. twin sisters

    B. welcome visitors

    C. drop by

    D. whenever I could

23. What is the meaning of the idiom in italics?

Let's *give a big hand* for a job well done.

A. offer assistance

B. pay a large sum

C. smash down

D. applaud loudly

24. Which of the following sentences contain an idiom that means "arrived"?

A. "Let's get this show on the road!" the bandleader told the band.

B. Janis finally showed up for her appointment, but she was over an hour late.

C. The receptionist showed the visitors up the stairs and told them to wait there.

D. The Red Sox played so well, they finally showed up their great rival, the Yankees.

Grammar

25. Which of the following sentences uses capitalization correctly?

A. My brother said, "If you go to the movies, please take me along."

B. My brother said, "if you go to the movies, please take me along."

C. my brother said, "If you go to the movies, please take me along."

D. my brother said, "if you go to the movies, please take me along."

26. Which of the following sentences is capitalized correctly?

A. Jo and Anne went to a Portuguese Restaurant after they visited the Newark Museum.

B. Jo and Anne went to a portuguese restaurant after they visited the Newark museum.

C. Jo and Anne went to a Portuguese restaurant after they visited the Newark Museum.

D. Jo and anne went to a Portuguese restaurant after they visited the Newark museum.

27. Which statement about abbreviations is true?

A. Abbreviations are usually longer than the word or words they stand for.

B. Abbreviations always start with a capital letter.

C. Abbreviations usually end with a period.

D. Abbreviations never include letters that are not in the word they stand for.

28. Which of the following phrases uses abbreviations correctly?

A. Martin Luther King Jr

B. JAN 23, 2007

C. 55 San Andreas Bvd.

D. Dr. Sheldon L. Greenfarb

29. Which pronoun correctly completes the following sentence?

Carlos and _____ are planning to read that best seller.

A. I

B. me

C. myself

D. mine

30. Which of the following sentences uses pronouns correctly?
    A. The stars of the game were Jackie and her.
    B. The stars of the game were Jackie and she.
    C. Larry and him scored some points in the first quarter.
    D. The crowd cheered loudly for Larry and he.

Spelling

31. Which of the following words is spelled correctly?
    A. oxugen
    B. cematery
    C. catagory
    D. medicine

32. In which sentence is the italic word spelled correctly?
    A. The police officers gathered *evadence* at the crime scene.
    B. If you *multeply* by 2, the answer is always an even number.
    C. Do not *abandon* hope yet; help is on the way.
    D. The teacher knew the subject but had trouble with *disapline*.

33. Which statement about spelling is correct?
    A. The sound of "uh" is usually spelled with an *a*.
    B. The sound of "uh" is usually spelled with an *e*.
    C. The sound of "uh" is usually spelled with an *i* or a *u*.
    D. The sound of "uh" is usually spelled with a vowel.

ESSAY

Writing

34. Recall a folk tale or another story from the oral tradition, such as a fairy tale or a myth. It might be a story you read recently or in the past, or even one you had read to you as a child. On your paper or on a separate sheet, write a summary of the tale.

35. Think about why you remembered the tale you summarized in the previous question. Then, on your paper or on a separate sheet, write a one-paragraph review of the tale. Be sure to indicate whether or not you recommend that others read it.

36. Think about subjects that interest you and that you would like to know more about. Then, on your paper, write down your idea for a subject that you could investigate for a research report. Also list at least three information sources that would probably provide good information on the subject.

ANSWERS

"Grasshopper Logic," "The Other Frog Prince,"
and "duckbilled platypus vs. beefsnakstik®"
by Jon Scieszka and Lane Smith

Vocabulary Warm-up Exercises, p. 2

A.
1. bragged
2. plenty
3. fur
4. pathetic
5. hopped
6. promptly
7. wiped
8. moral

B. Sample Answers
1. When the princess arrived, the photographers wanted to take her picture.
2. Mammals, such as horses and dogs, are warm-blooded animals.
3. The wicked boss always treated his employees unfairly.
4. The logic of the witches' spell was not easy to comprehend.
5. If you rewrite your assignment, it is a second draft of your work.
6. The production of the play is meant to be seen live on stage.

Reading Warm-up A, p. 3

Sample Answers
1. (doing a dance to celebrate the easy life of summer); Hopped means "jumped or leaped in a short, springing motion."
2. (the sweat from his brow); Kristen used the eraser when she wiped the chalk off the board.
3. to eat; In my home, there are plenty of towels and cans of soup.
4. (It will help me keep warm during the cold days of winter.); Fur is "the soft, thick hair covering many mammals."
5. my comfortable hammock and shady home; Billy bragged that he was the best chess player in the county.
6. (continued on his way); I have promptly reported for my babysitting job.
7. shivered in the cold. He could find no food anywhere.; It is a pathetic sight when people do not have enough warm clothes to wear.
8. Plan ahead for the days of necessity. A moral is "a lesson taught by a fable."

Reading Warm-up B, p. 4

Sample Answers
1. fairy tales and legends; make-believe stories that have been handed down through time; these fantastic stories; A princess is "the daughter of a king or queen."
2. (witch); The evil man told a wicked lie.
3. (a wizard); A magician, a witch, or a genie might cast a spell.
4. a rabbit and a fox; Other mammals are bats, dogs, and opossums.
5. that many similar stories come from different parts of the world; History means "a course that studies the recorded past events of the world."
6. (has never been proved); It is not good logic to assume you will pass the test if you do not study.
7. (many old stories that are based on legends and folk-tales); I once had to rewrite a poem and make it into a story for my language arts class.
8. of a play; I have seen a production of Romeo and Juliet.

Jon Scieszka

Listening and Viewing, p. 5

Sample answers and guidelines for evaluation:

Segment 1. Jon Scieszka chose a young audience as a result of his teaching experience, where he found that young readers are involved and enthusiastic about stories. Scieszka read Dr. Seuss books, comics, and adventure and mystery stories as a young student. Students may suggest that his diverse reading helps him to come up with creative ways to retell the information he gathers from reading to a young audience.

Segment 2. Jon Scieszka is amazed that these stories have been around for hundreds of years and are still relevant to today's reader. Students may answer that it is important to tell these stories to ensure the stories' survival and to teach kids lessons and common knowledge often taught in these tales.

Segment 3. Lane Smith illustrates Jon Scieszka's books; Smith comes up with the visual representation of Jon Scieszka's ideas and brings them to life on the page. Students may answer that illustrations are important to these stories because they add excitement and detail.

Segment 4. Jon Scieszka likes being able to connect with a wide audience and teach many people through his stories. Students may suggest that reading is important because it allows people to learn more about the world around them as well as more about themselves. Reading is also a creative activity, which allows readers to use their imaginations more, unlike television and video games.

Unit 6: Learning About the Oral Tradition, p. 6

A.
1. hyperbole
2. myth
3. legend
4. personification
5. moral

B. Plot summaries will vary but should include one or more animals with human characteristics. The fable should end with a moral that defines the lesson that the animal or animals learned.

"Grasshopper Logic," "The Other Frog Prince," and "duckbilled platypus vs. beefsnakstik®"
by Jon Scieszka and Lane Smith

Model Selection: The Oral Tradition, p. 7

A. 1. The homework assignment is an example of hyperbole. It is greatly exaggerated.

2. In the traditional fairy tale, the frog turns into a handsome prince when the princess kisses him.

3. They are a mammal and a beef snack food stick. They speak like humans, and they try to outdo each other.

B. The grasshopper speaks and acts like a human boy who wants to hang out with his friends after school rather than start his homework. His mother acts like a human mother, wanting her son to complete his assignment.

Selection Test A, p. 8

Learning About the Oral Tradition

1. ANS: A	DIF: Easy	OBJ: Literary Analysis
2. ANS: C	DIF: Easy	OBJ: Literary Analysis
3. ANS: A	DIF: Easy	OBJ: Literary Analysis
4. ANS: D	DIF: Easy	OBJ: Literary Analysis
5. ANS: C	DIF: Easy	OBJ: Literary Analysis

Critical Reading

6. ANS: A	DIF: Easy	OBJ: Comprehension
7. ANS: B	DIF: Easy	OBJ: Literary Analysis
8. ANS: B	DIF: Easy	OBJ: Interpretation
9. ANS: C	DIF: Easy	OBJ: Interpretation
10. ANS: D	DIF: Easy	OBJ: Comprehension
11. ANS: A	DIF: Easy	OBJ: Literary Analysis
12. ANS: B	DIF: Easy	OBJ: Comprehension
13. ANS: D	DIF: Easy	OBJ: Comprehension
14. ANS: D	DIF: Easy	OBJ: Literary Analysis
15. ANS: A	DIF: Easy	OBJ: Literary Analysis

Essay

16. Answers will vary but should be supported by details from the story. Students may say that the princess feels surprised and maybe a bit foolish. She probably expected the frog to turn into a handsome prince and that they would live "happily ever after" together.

Difficulty: *Easy*

Objective: *Essay*

17. Students should state that "Grasshopper Logic" is a fable. It features grasshoppers that are personified and speak and act like humans. The moral is directly stated at the end "There are plenty of things to say to calm a hopping mad Grasshopper mom. 'I don't know' is not one."

Difficulty: *Easy*

Objective: *Essay*

Selection Test B, p. 11

Learning About the Oral Tradition

1. ANS: D	DIF: Average	OBJ: Literary Analysis
2. ANS: C	DIF: Challenging	OBJ: Literary Analysis
3. ANS: A	DIF: Average	OBJ: Literary Analysis
4. ANS: C	DIF: Average	OBJ: Literary Analysis
5. ANS: B	DIF: Average	OBJ: Literary Analysis
6. ANS: D	DIF: Challenging	OBJ: Literary Analysis

Critical Reading

7. ANS: B	DIF: Average	OBJ: Comprehension
8. ANS: D	DIF: Average	OBJ: Comprehension
9. ANS: A	DIF: Average	OBJ: Comprehension
10. ANS: D	DIF: Average	OBJ: Literary Analysis
11. ANS: C	DIF: Challenging	OBJ: Interpretation
12. ANS: B	DIF: Average	OBJ: Comprehension
13. ANS: A	DIF: Average	OBJ: Interpretation
14. ANS: B	DIF: Average	OBJ: Literary Analysis
15. ANS: A	DIF: Challenging	OBJ: Interpretation
16. ANS: D	DIF: Average	OBJ: Literary Analysis
17. ANS: A	DIF: Challenging	OBJ: Interpretation
18. ANS: B	DIF: Challenging	OBJ: Literary Analysis
19. ANS: C	DIF: Average	OBJ: Interpretation

Essay

20. Answers will vary. Students should effectively retell the main ideas of the story from the princess's point of view, showing her thoughts and feelings regarding the appearance of the frog, the trick he played on her, and her feelings about being tricked into kissing a frog.

Difficulty: *Average*

Objective: *Essay*

21. Students may say that the mother will help Grasshopper with his huge assignment, or that she will scold him. Students may predict that Grasshopper will learn his lesson after his mother scolds him. All answers should be logical predictions, based on story events.

Difficulty: *Average*

Objective: *Essay*

22. Answers will vary. Students may say that the moral is similar to "Do not believe everything you hear," "Never trust a sad frog," or "Find out more about people before you trust them." All suggested morals should be supported with details from the story.

Difficulty: *Challenging*

Objective: *Essay*

Unit 6, Part 1 Answers

Diagnostic Test 11, p. 15

MULTIPLE CHOICE

1. ANS: A
2. ANS: D
3. ANS: A
4. ANS: C
5. ANS: B
6. ANS: B
7. ANS: C
8. ANS: C
9. ANS: D
10. ANS: B
11. ANS: A
12. ANS: A
13. ANS: D
14. ANS: B
15. ANS: C

"Icarus and Daedalus"
by Josephine Preston Peabody

Vocabulary Warm-up Exercises, p. 19

A.
1. glimpse
2. captive
3. thirst
4. delay
5. fashioned
6. attempt
7. liberty
8. favor

B. Sample Answers
1. The company hired an <u>architect</u> to design a new office building.
2. The <u>imprisoned</u> man missed his freedom.
3. The customer ordered water to <u>quench</u> his thirst.
4. Amy listened to her mom's <u>cautions</u> and always wore a helmet when riding her bike.
5. The acrobat <u>sustained</u> three other acrobats on his shoulders thanks to his upper body strength.
6. The athlete won the race after he <u>overtook</u> the lead runner at the last minute.
7. When the car wheels <u>wavered</u>, Michael decreased the speed.

Reading Warm-up A, p. 20

Sample Answers

1. (failed); Every *try* failed, but that did not stop people from trying.
2. (unimaginable freedom); *Glimpse* means "a brief, quick view."
3. (freedom); My mom gives me the *liberty* to choose my own clothes.
4. (desire); I have a *desire* for travel and adventure.
5. <u>500 years</u>; A *delay* is "a length of time spent waiting."
6. <u>aluminum tubes</u>, <u>synthetic fiber</u>; A synonym for *fashioned* is *made from*.
7. (approval); I seek my teacher's *favor*.
8. (set free); Someone might be *captive* during wartime when held by the enemy.

Reading Warm-up B, p. 21

Sample Answers

1. (up, up, and up); Smoke billowing from a chimney goes *aloft*; so does a hot-air balloon.
2. <u>in a cramped cabin</u>; I feel *imprisoned* during long drives in a car with my little brother.
3. <u>between flying and taking the train</u>; *Back and forth* means the same thing as wavered.
4. <u>(sparkling water)</u>; *Quench* means "to satisfy."
5. <u>designed billion-dollar buildings</u>; My mom hired an *architect* to design our new home.
6. <u>He checked his seat belt: buckled. He checked the emergency exit: three rows back. The cautions</u>; The *cautions* I take most seriously are to buckle my seat belt in a car and to never walk alone once it gets dark.
7. (air); *Supported* is a synonym for *sustained*.
8. (sleep); *Overtook* means "to catch up with."

"Icarus and Daedalus"
by Josephine Preston Peabody

Reading: Ask Questions to Analyze Cause-and-Effect Relationships, p. 22

Sample Answers

1. *Effect:* He has Daedalus put in prison. *Effect:* Daedalus escapes from prison.
2. *Question:* What happens as a result of Daedalus's watching the sea-gulls? *Effect:* Daedalus realizes that the only way to escape is by flying. *Effect:* Daedalus makes a set of wings.
3. *Question:* What happens as a result of Daedalus's warning? *Effect:* Icarus ignores the warning. *Effect:* Icarus flies too close to the sun.

Literary Analysis: Myth, p. 23

Sample Answers

1. The excerpt shows a human hero with superhuman traits. The excerpt refers to Daedalus as a mortal who "learned the secrets of the gods."

2. The excerpt explores a universal theme. Daedalus is telling Icarus something that every parent might tell a child: Do not go to extremes; act in moderation.

3. The excerpt expresses ideas about right and wrong. Daedalus makes an offering to a god and gives up the idea of flying. This shows that Daedalus admits he was wrong to try to act like a god by doing something humans are not naturally able to do.

   Note: Students may instead say that the excerpt explains a natural occurrence—how Icaria got its name, or they may link this excerpt to the exploration of a universal theme.

Vocabulary Builder, p. 24

A. Sample answers follow the yes or no designation:

1. No; "no vacancy" means that all the rooms have been taken, so one could not get a room at the motel.

2. Yes; the politicians' promises supported the villagers' hopes; the villagers believed the promises would be fulfilled.

B. Sample Answers

1. The vacancy in the look on the man's face made me think that he had nothing on his mind.

2. Sustained by the food, the villagers had no fears of starving.

C. 1. C; 2. A

Enrichment: Greek Gods and Modern English, p. 27

A. 1. atlas
2. Herculean
3. *Titanic*
4. chronological
5. chaotic
6. plutonium

B. Students should use the words in grammatically correct sentences. Sample answers:

You can look at an atlas if you want to see where the *Titanic* struck the iceberg. If you do not tell what happened in chronological order, your story is likely to be chaotic. The discovery of plutonium was a Herculean undertaking.

Selection Test A, p. 28

Critical Reading

1. ANS: B	DIF: Easy	OBJ: Reading
2. ANS: A	DIF: Easy	OBJ: Interpretation
3. ANS: B	DIF: Easy	OBJ: Interpretation
4. ANS: D	DIF: Easy	OBJ: Comprehension
5. ANS: B	DIF: Easy	OBJ: Reading
6. ANS: D	DIF: Easy	OBJ: Reading
7. ANS: B	DIF: Easy	OBJ: Comprehension
8. ANS: C	DIF: Easy	OBJ: Literary Analysis
9. ANS: D	DIF: Easy	OBJ: Interpretation
10. ANS: C	DIF: Easy	OBJ: Interpretation

Vocabulary and Grammar

11. ANS: B	DIF: Easy	OBJ: Vocabulary
12. ANS: C	DIF: Easy	OBJ: Vocabulary
13. ANS: D	DIF: Easy	OBJ: Grammar
14. ANS: A	DIF: Easy	OBJ: Grammar

Essay

15. Students who prefer Icarus may say that they can relate to his desire to ignore his father's warnings; those who prefer Daedalus may say that they are impressed with his ingenuity. In any case, students should offer a well-thought-out explanation and cite two details from the selection to support their points.

   Difficulty: *Easy*

   Objective: *Essay*

16. In stating whether they believe Daedalus shared in the responsibility for his son's death, students should refer to the warnings Daedalus offers and evaluate whether they were adequate. Students might also comment on whether a lifetime of imprisonment would have been preferable to the risk involved in attempting to flee.

   Difficulty: *Easy*

   Objective: *Essay*

Selection Test B, p. 31

Critical Reading

1. ANS: C	DIF: Average	OBJ: Comprehension
2. ANS: B	DIF: Average	OBJ: Interpretation
3. ANS: D	DIF: Average	OBJ: Reading
4. ANS: D	DIF: Average	OBJ: Comprehension
5. ANS: B	DIF: Average	OBJ: Comprehension
6. ANS: D	DIF: Challenging	OBJ: Interpretation
7. ANS: B	DIF: Average	OBJ: Interpretation
8. ANS: B	DIF: Average	OBJ: Comprehension
9. ANS: D	DIF: Average	OBJ: Reading
10. ANS: D	DIF: Challenging	OBJ: Interpretation
11. ANS: C	DIF: Challenging	OBJ: Comprehension
12. ANS: C	DIF: Average	OBJ: Literary Analysis
13. ANS: D	DIF: Challenging	OBJ: Literary Analysis
14. ANS: A	DIF: Challenging	OBJ: Literary Analysis

Vocabulary and Grammar

15. ANS: C   DIF: Average   OBJ: Vocabulary
16. ANS: D   DIF: Challenging   OBJ: Vocabulary
17. ANS: B   DIF: Average   OBJ: Grammar
18. ANS: C   DIF: Average   OBJ: Grammar

Essay

19. Students should recognize that Daedalus warns Icarus to fly neither too low (lest he be weighed down by the fog) nor too high (lest the heat of the sun melt the wax that secures the feathers to the wings). They should note that if Icarus had heeded his father's warning and flown a middle course, he would have followed Daedalus to safety.

    Difficulty: *Average*

    Objective: *Essay*

20. If students note that the narrator of the myth suggests that Daedalus was overreaching, they are likely to conclude that he should never have attempted the flight. If they believe that Daedalus was justified in attempting the escape, they should evaluate his warnings to Icarus and provide a credible argument in support of or in opposition to the idea that Daedalus shares in the responsibility for Icarus's death. They may say, for example, that as the father, Daedalus was solely responsible for his son's well being; or they may say that Icarus received sufficient warning, and a parent can do only so much to protect a child.

    Difficulty: *Average*

    Objective: *Essay*

21. Students should refer to the selection to support their description of Daedalus's character. They might note, for example, that Daedalus "learned the secrets of the gods," which in the context of a Greek myth is considered a negative characteristic. He also invented the Labyrinth, which was meant to fool people, and he may have used deception to escape from the prison cell. As positive traits, students will likely point to Daedalus's ingenuity in inventing a human-powered means of flight and his great love of his son (although they may argue that he did not do enough to ensure Icarus's safety).

    Difficulty: *Challenging*

    Objective: *Essay*

"Demeter and Persephone" by Anne Terry White

Vocabulary Warm-up Exercises, p. 35

A. 1. fertile
2. toiled
3. harvest
4. joyful
5. descend
6. goddess
7. innocent
8. grim

B. Sample Answers
1. Parents should not reward a child who *defies* them because he or she is refusing to do as told.
2. You would not call a doctor because a *pang* is a feeling of discomfort, not a health problem.
3. I would wear boots because sandals would not protect my feet from the *thistles*.
4. A man who owns a *chariot* would need hay to feed the horse that pulls it.
5. A heavy *fragrance* will not keep me warm because it is just a smell.
6. A train moving forward *mightily* is moving too fast and too forcefully to jump on.
7. Another *realm* is another place, so you would not be at home.

Reading Warm-up A, p. 36

Sample Answers

1. ruled over mankind; Diana is the goddess of the moon.
2. (cheerful); In fact, he was downright *gloomy* compared with his brothers, Zeus and Poseidon.
3. (barren); *Fertile* means "fruitful" or "good for growing crops."
4. fed humankind; The farmer stored his wheat *harvest* beside the barn.
5. into the land of Hades; How can she *descend* the staircase in high heels and a ball gown without tripping?
6. (guilty); *Innocent* means "not to be guilty of anything."
7. in the fields; I have *toiled* to make my term paper great.
8. (happy-go-lucky); I think holiday music and festive lights are *joyful*.

Reading Warm-up B, p. 37

Sample Answers

1. (kingdom); I visited the *realm* of Great Britain.
2. prickly plant; You might find *thistles* growing in a forest or a garden.
3. of stage fright; he was feeling *twinges* of stage fright
4. (struggled); The lost kitten cried *weakly* for its mother.
5. (in his neck); *Veins* are the tubes that carry blood to all parts of the body.
6. (disobeys); Mom gets angry with my brother when he *defies* her orders.
7. (two-wheeled vehicle); You might find a *chariot* in the Coliseum during the time of the Roman Empire.
8. (smell); My favorite *fragrance* is the smell of tea roses.

"Demeter and Persephone" by Anne Terry White

Reading: Ask Questions to Analyze Cause-and-Effect Relationships, p. 38

Sample Answers

1. *Effect:* Pluto falls in love with Persephone. *Effect:* Pluto kidnaps Persephone and takes her to the underworld.
2. *Question:* What happens as a result of Persephone's being held captive in the underworld? *Effect:* Demeter blames the earth for Persephone's disappearance. *Effect:* Zeus sends Hermes to bring Persephone back from the underworld.
3. *Question:* What happens as a result of Persephone's eating the pomegranate seeds? *Effect:* She must return to the underworld for four months of every year. *Effect:* Earth experiences winter, the season that Persephone spends in the underworld.

Literary Analysis: Myth, p. 39

Sample Answers

1. The excerpt explains a natural occurrence volcanic activity. The passage refers to a real volcano, Mt. Aetna, and to mythical creatures.
2. The excerpt shows a god with human traits. Pluto, a god, is described as falling in love just the way a human being might.
3. The excerpt expresses a belief about right and wrong. It refers to the famine that Demeter causes on earth as a result of her grief, and it shows Zeus's reaction. Zeus is saying that it is wrong to punish people for something they did not do.

Vocabulary Builder, p. 40

Sample Answers

A. 1. A soldier who defies orders is boldly refusing to follow orders, so he or she is likely to be punished.
   2. If you intervene in a fight, you get in the middle of it, so you might get hurt.

B. 1. Zeus becomes angry when a god or goddess defies his orders.
   2. When there is trouble, Zeus is likely to intervene.

C. 1. B; 2. C

Enrichment: Gods and Goddesses in Greek Mythology, p. 43

A. 1. Persephone
   2. Poseidon
   3. Apollo
   4. Athena
   5. Ares, Nike
   6. Zeus
   7. Demeter

B. Students should name at least two gods and/or goddesses and suggest actors or actresses to play the roles. They should offer logical explanations for their choices.

"Icarus and Daedalus"
by Josephine Preston Peabody
"Demeter and Persephone" by Anne Terry White

Build Language Skills: Vocabulary, p. 44

Sample Answers

A. 1. *Definition:* a person admired for his or her accomplishments; *Connotation:* positive; *Sentence:* The firefighter who saved the baby's life was hailed as a hero.
   2. *Definition:* exaggerating one's own importance; *Connotation:* negative; *Sentence:* The arrogant scholar was despised by her colleagues.

B. 1. A player's illness would have an effect on his or her soccer game because he or she would most likely not be able to perform well.
   2. A slippery sidewalk will affect the speed at which people walk because they will most likely slow down so they do not fall.
   3. As a consequence of learning to play the trumpet, one might have an opportunity to play in a band.
   4. If someone breaks the law, he or she might be charged with a crime, and a trial might then occur.
   5. I might alter my routine if I find that I am not working efficiently.

Build Language Skills: Grammar, p. 45

A. 1. All of the characters in "Demeter and Persephone" are gods or goddesses: Aphrodite, Eros, Pluto, Persephone, Demeter, Zeus, and Hermes.
   2. Daedalus warns Icarus not to do these things: fly too low, fly too high, and fly too far from him.

B. Guidelines for evaluation: Students should write two grammatically correct sentences that include a colon followed by a list of items.

"Demeter and Persephone" by Anne Terry White

Selection Test A, p. 46

Critical Reading

1. ANS: B	DIF: Easy	OBJ: Reading
2. ANS: B	DIF: Easy	OBJ: Reading
3. ANS: D	DIF: Easy	OBJ: Comprehension
4. ANS: A	DIF: Easy	OBJ: Interpretation
5. ANS: B	DIF: Easy	OBJ: Reading
6. ANS: A	DIF: Easy	OBJ: Comprehension
7. ANS: B	DIF: Easy	OBJ: Interpretation

8. ANS: A	DIF: Easy	OBJ: Reading
9. ANS: C	DIF: Easy	OBJ: Comprehension
10. ANS: D	DIF: Easy	OBJ: Literary Analysis
11. ANS: B	DIF: Easy	OBJ: Literary Analysis
12. ANS: C	DIF: Easy	OBJ: Literary Analysis

Vocabulary and Grammar

13. ANS: A	DIF: Easy	OBJ: Vocabulary
14. ANS: B	DIF: Easy	OBJ: Vocabulary
15. ANS: C	DIF: Easy	OBJ: Grammar

Essay

16. Students should describe the character they prefer, including two details about the character to support their explanation.
Difficulty: *Easy*
Objective: *Essay*

17. Students should state a point of view and provide two details from the selection to support their argument.
Difficulty: *Easy*
Objective: *Essay*

Selection Test B, p. 49

Critical Reading

1. ANS: D	DIF: Challenging	OBJ: Interpretation
2. ANS: A	DIF: Average	OBJ: Interpretation
3. ANS: C	DIF: Challenging	OBJ: Comprehension
4. ANS: D	DIF: Average	OBJ: Comprehension
5. ANS: B	DIF: Average	OBJ: Reading
6. ANS: C	DIF: Average	OBJ: Comprehension
7. ANS: C	DIF: Challenging	OBJ: Interpretation
8. ANS: C	DIF: Average	OBJ: Comprehension
9. ANS: A	DIF: Challenging	OBJ: Interpretation
10. ANS: A	DIF: Average	OBJ: Reading
11. ANS: A	DIF: Average	OBJ: Literary Analysis
12. ANS: C	DIF: Average	OBJ: Interpretation
13. ANS: A	DIF: Challenging	OBJ: Literary Analysis
14. ANS: D	DIF: Average	OBJ: Interpretation
15. ANS: D	DIF: Challenging	OBJ: Literary Analysis
16. ANS: C	DIF: Average	OBJ: Literary Analysis

Vocabulary and Grammar

17. ANS: A	DIF: Average	OBJ: Vocabulary
18. ANS: D	DIF: Average	OBJ: Vocabulary
19. ANS: A	DIF: Average	OBJ: Grammar
20. ANS: D	DIF: Average	OBJ: Grammar

Essay

21. Students who choose Eros should note that if he had not shot Pluto with the arrow of love, Pluto would never have kidnapped Persephone. Students who choose Pluto should note that he acts selfishly by keeping Persephone with him against her will. Students who choose Demeter should note that she need not have punished the earth for Persephone's disappearance.
Difficulty: *Average*
Objective: *Essay*

22. Students should recognize that the myth suggests that love is an overpowering emotion, one that is not based on rational thought.
Difficulty: *Average*
Objective: *Essay*

23. Students should recognize that the gods share with humans one or more of the following traits: They fall in love, have familial relationships, and possess different skills and abilities. Students should also recognize that, unlike humans, gods have the following characteristics: the power to imprison some beings under the earth, the ability to make gods fall in love, the ability to travel to different realms (such as the underworld), and the ability to affect the natural order of things on earth.
Difficulty: *Challenging*
Objective: *Essay*

"Tenochtitlan: Inside the Aztec Capital"
by Jacqueline Dineen

Vocabulary Warm-up Exercises, p. 53

A. 1. described
   2. adobe
   3. gaps
   4. fibers
   5. excellent
   6. prevented
   7. included
   8. historical

B. Sample Answers

1. On the *site* of an abandoned campground, I might find a picnic table, ashes from a fire, and extra firewood.

2. To plant some flowers, I would use the following *utensils*: a hoe, a trowel, and a spade.

3. The usual cure for an *enchanted* princess is a kiss from the handsome prince.

4. If I had fireplaces but no *chimneys* in a house, the house would fill with smoke whenever a fire was lit.

5. One advantage to living in *compounds* rather than in separate dwellings is companionship.

6. If I joined *households* with my best friend, *(answers will vary)* people would be living together.

7. One way *grandchildren* can show their love for grandparents is to spend time with them.
8. I prefer *courtyards* to back yards because I like the idea of having access to the outdoors from all parts of the house.

Reading Warm-up A, p. 54

Sample Answers

1. building material; *Adobe* is commonly seen in the southwestern part of the U.S.
2. (ancient); A *historical* event that I wish I could have seen in person is the inauguration of John F. Kennedy.
3. hay or grass; *Fibers* are threads or threadlike parts, as of a fabric or of animal or plant tissue.
4. (between the bricks); The word *gaps* means "cracks or openings, as in a wall."
5. shrinkage; I once *prevented* a behavior problem with my dog by taking him to obedience school.
6. (Pink or ochre pigments); Access to the pool is *included* with the price of admission.
7. material; I would like to be *described* as friendly and generous.
8. (it needs little maintenance); One *excellent* choice I made recently was to finish my homework rather than watch TV.

Reading Warm-up B, p. 55

Sample Answers

1. their way of life; As the children walked through the *enchanted* forest, the trees came to life.
2. (individual); *Households* means "families; people who live under the same roof."
3. different generations living in different wings of the home and sharing common space in the middle; *Compounds* means "walled yards with buildings in them."
4. (see each other every day); Carl's *grandchildren* all lived at least a hundred miles away from him.
5. picturesque; The *site* for a home I'd like to have would be high on a hill, overlooking the city lights.
6. (gather and visit); *Courtyards* means "open spaces surrounded by walls."
7. fireplaces; Without *chimneys*, we couldn't have fireplaces in our homes.
8. (dishes, glasses); *Utensils* are tools, implements, or containers used to do or make something.

"Tenochtitlan: Inside the Aztec Capital"
by Jacqueline Dineen

Reading: Reread to Look for Connections That Indicate Cause-and-Effect Relationships, p. 56

1. cause
2. Therefore; cause and effect

3. Because of; cause and effect
4. As a result; effect
5. cause
6. Because; cause and effect
7. cause and effect
8. Because; cause and effect
9. Because; effect
10. cause
11. For that reason; cause and effect
12. effect

Literary Analysis: Legends and Facts, p. 57

Sample answers follow the designation of fact or speculation:

1. Fact; this information can be proved true based on written records or excavated ruins.
2. Fact; this information can be proved true based on written records or excavated ruins.
3. Fact; this information can be proved true based on Bernal Diaz's description.
4. Fact; this information can be proved true based on excavated ruins and observation.
5. Speculation; the word *think* indicates that the information has not been proved true.
6. Speculation; the words *are not sure* and *think* indicate that the information has not been proved true.
7. Speculation; the words *must have been* indicate that the information is not known to be true.

Vocabulary Builder, p. 58

A. Sample answers follow the yes or no designation:

1. No, the outskirts of a city are far from the center, and the Temple Mayor was in the center of Tenochtitlan.
2. No, reeds are grasses, not trees.
3. No, he was serving a beverage; goblets are cups.

B. Sample Answers

1. Michael liked living on the outskirts of the city so that he could be far from the center of activity.
2. The builders could not use reeds for the foundation, because they are not strong enough to bear the weight of a three-story house.
3. The servants poured water into the goblets.

C. 1. B; 2. D; 3. A

Enrichment: Aztec Words in English, p. 61

1. chili
2. ocelot
3. shack
4. chocolate
5. mesquite
6. tomato
7. avocado

8. pulque
9. coyote
10. tamale

Selection Test A, p. 62
Critical Reading

1. ANS: B	DIF: Easy	OBJ: Literary Analysis
2. ANS: C	DIF: Easy	OBJ: Comprehension
3. ANS: B	DIF: Easy	OBJ: Reading
4. ANS: D	DIF: Easy	OBJ: Comprehension
5. ANS: A	DIF: Easy	OBJ: Comprehension
6. ANS: D	DIF: Easy	OBJ: Comprehension
7. ANS: C	DIF: Easy	OBJ: Comprehension
8. ANS: D	DIF: Easy	OBJ: Comprehension
9. ANS: B	DIF: Easy	OBJ: Literary Analysis
10. ANS: A	DIF: Easy	OBJ: Comprehension
11. ANS: B	DIF: Easy	OBJ: Interpretation
12. ANS: B	DIF: Easy	OBJ: Comprehension

Vocabulary and Grammar

13. ANS: C	DIF: Easy	OBJ: Vocabulary
14. ANS: A	DIF: Easy	OBJ: Grammar

Essay

15. Students should conclude that Dineen wrote about Tenochtitlan to inform readers about the city that was the capital of the Aztec empire hundreds of years ago. Evidence should include any fact related to the history of the city, its layout, the skill of the Aztec engineers, and the way in which the Aztecs lived.

    Difficulty: *Easy*

    Objective: *Essay*

16. Students should describe one solution devised by the Aztecs in response to a problem presented by one of the situations. Students may say, for example, that because Tenochtitlan was built on an island in a lake, the Aztecs built causeways linking the city to the mainland, or they may say that the Aztecs built canals, on which they traveled by canoe. In response to the second situation, they may note that city residents imported food from outside the city, kept turkeys for food and eggs, and drained additional land for farming. The important point is that students should recognize a cause-and-effect relationship, noting something the Aztecs did in response to something else.

    Difficulty: *Easy*

    Objective: *Essay*

Selection Test B, p. 65
Critical Reading

1. ANS: B	DIF: Average	OBJ: Literary Analysis
2. ANS: D	DIF: Challenging	OBJ: Comprehension
3. ANS: C	DIF: Average	OBJ: Reading
4. ANS: C	DIF: Average	OBJ: Interpretation
5. ANS: B	DIF: Average	OBJ: Comprehension
6. ANS: A	DIF: Average	OBJ: Comprehension
7. ANS: A	DIF: Average	OBJ: Literary Analysis
8. ANS: D	DIF: Challenging	OBJ: Literary Analysis
9. ANS: B	DIF: Challenging	OBJ: Interpretation
10. ANS: C	DIF: Challenging	OBJ: Interpretation
11. ANS: A	DIF: Average	OBJ: Reading
12. ANS: B	DIF: Average	OBJ: Reading
13. ANS: D	DIF: Average	OBJ: Comprehension
14. ANS: A	DIF: Average	OBJ: Comprehension

Vocabulary and Grammar

15. ANS: B	DIF: Challenging	OBJ: Vocabulary
16. ANS: A	DIF: Average	OBJ: Vocabulary
17. ANS: A	DIF: Average	OBJ: Grammar
18. ANS: C	DIF: Average	OBJ: Grammar

Essay

19. Students should note that in addition to an emperor, there were priests and nobles. They should point out that no more than half the population is thought to have been farmers, and the rest were craftspeople and nobles. Students may cite other details about the distinctions between the homes of the nobles and the poorer people.

    Difficulty: *Average*

    Objective: *Essay*

20. Students should cite at least two of these accomplishments: To irrigate the land, the Aztecs dug ditches; they piled up the earth from the ditches and used it for farming; they built an embankment to keep out salt water and prevent flooding. Students might point out that no more than half the population were farmers, so food was imported, and they may note that farmers grew corn, tomatoes, beans, chili peppers, prickly pears, and maguey cacti and raised turkey for meat and eggs.

    Difficulty: *Average*

    Objective: *Essay*

21. Students should recall at least two facts relating to the illustration they choose. For example, they should note that the map shows the layout of the causeways, the location of the central temple, and how each group of houses could be reached by a causeway. The photograph of the maguey cactus indicates its size, and the caption describes its many uses. The drawing of the emperor's palace shows its size, and the caption explains the purpose of several of its rooms.

Difficulty: *Challenging*

Objective: *Essay*

"Popocatepetl and Ixtlaccihuatl"
by Julie Piggott Wood

Vocabulary Warm-up Exercises, p. 69

A.
1. emperor
2. conflict
3. peril
4. behalf
5. coastal
6. capital
7. siege
8. capacity

B. Sample Answers
1. No, I would not be proud to take a *bribe* because it is a payment for doing something wrong.
2. If my job were to *reign* over a country, my first act would be to declare longer weekends.
3. A dog who *exhibited* fear might put its tail between its legs and slink away, whining.
4. If I wanted to make a *pyramid* shape out of paper, I would need to cut out a square or a rectangle for the base and several triangles for the sides.
5. I need *approximately* one hour to get ready for school in the morning.
6. A ideal meal that has foods from a *variety* of food groups might include grilled fish, steamed rice, green beans, a green salad, bread, and a fruit assortment with cheese.
7. The *expected* outcome of a series of swim lessons is the ability to swim.
8. At the site of a burned-down house, I might find *fragments* such as broken dishes, shattered mirrors, and broken glass.

Reading Warm-up A, p. 70

Sample Answers
1. Mexico and Central America; A *coastal* area I would especially like to visit is the coast of Oregon because of its rugged beauty.
2. (for adventure); I have a great *capacity* for humor.
3. shipwreck; One *peril* that I have survived is swimming in an area where there were lots of jellyfish.

4. (Montezuma); Once, I acted on my sister's *behalf* when I returned a purchase she didn't want.
5. ruler; *Emperor* means "a person who rules over a group of different states, nations, or territories."
6. (Tenochtitlan); The *capital* of my state is Sacramento.
7. several months; *Siege* means "steady and persistent attempt to win something."
8. (By the spring of the following year); Recently, I had a *conflict* with my best friend over who should be invited to my birthday party.

Reading Warm-up B, p. 71

Sample Answers
1. Aztec; It would be fun to climb to the top of a *pyramid*.
2. (broke off); We used *fragments* of the broken china in our mosaic.
3. Montezuma; *Reign* means "the period during which a monarch rules."
4. (five minutes); *Approximately* means "about or around."
5. of hand signals; A *variety* of hand signals that I use in everyday life include thumbs up for "okay," waving to express good-bye or hello, and holding my thumb and forefinger about an inch apart to mean "just a little."
6. (hostile behavior); Once my neighbor exhibited *hostile* behavior toward me when I accidentally tossed his newspaper at his front window.
7. of his adventure; If this story continued, I think Donnie would get back to the time machine and return home.
8. (guard); Stella tried to *bribe* Maurice to let her copy his homework, but Maurice said no.

"Popocatepetl and Ixtlaccihuatl"
by Julie Piggott Wood

Reading: Reread to Look for Connections That Indicate Cause-and-Effect Relationships, p. 72

1. cause
2. therefore; effect
3. because; effect
4. cause
5. As a result; cause and effect
6. Because; cause and effect
7. Because; cause and effect
8. cause
9. effect
10. Because; cause and effect
11. effect
12. effect
13. Therefore; cause and effect
14. effect
15. effect

Literary Analysis: Legends and Facts, p. 73

1. This passage is rooted in historical fact; it contains facts, information that can be proved true.
2. This passage is probably based on a historical fact; there may have been an emperor like the one described.
3. This passage describes a larger-than-life hero; the description of him as the one responsible for driving off the enemy is probably exaggerated.
4. This passage describes a fantastic event, pyramids turning into mountains.

Vocabulary Builder, p. 74

A. Sample Answers

1. He made an official pronouncement.
2. If the warriors' support for Popo had been unanimous, everyone would have supported him, no one would have lied to the Emperor, and Popo and Ixtla would have married.
3. Yes; the warriors who said that Popo was dead were lying. Other warriors could have proved they were wrong.
4. No; once the warriors completely defeated the enemy, there were no more battles.

B. 1. C; 2. A; 3. D; 4. B

Enrichment: Volcanoes, p. 77

Sample Answers

Cinder cone: Formation and composition Formed from violent eruptions through a single vent; largely composed of cinders; *Typical shape and size* a bowl-shaped crater at the top; usually rises no more than 1,000 feet above surrounding area; *Famous example* Parícutin in Mexico

Composite: Formation and composition Formed as magma rises to the surface and pushes through a system of conduits that lead to a central vent or a central cluster of vents; composed of alternating layers of lava, volcanic ash, and cinders; *Typical shape and size* steep sides and symmetrical cones; may rise as high as 8,000 feet above surrounding area; *Famous examples* Fuji in Japan, Mount St. Helens and Mount Rainier in Washington State

Shield: Formation and composition Formed when small, thick, rounded masses of lava pile up around a vent; *Typical shape and size* Broad, gentle sloping cone with a slightly rounded top (resembling a warrior's shield); may have a diameter as great as 4 miles and a height of 2,000 feet; *Famous example* Mauna Loa on Hawaii

Lava dome: Formation and composition Formed almost entirely from fluid lava flows that spread from a central vent or group of vents. *Typical shape and size* may have a craggy dome or short, steep sides; *Famous example* Mount Pelée in Martinique, in the Caribbean

"Tenochtitlan: Inside the Aztec Capital"
by Jacqueline Dineen
"Popocatepetl and Ixtlaccihuatl"
by Juliet Piggott Wood

Build Language Skills: Vocabulary, p. 78

A. 1. resolute
2. obstinate
3. agitated
4. excited

B. Sample Answers

1. An effect of a long-term drought might be an inadequate supply of fresh water.
2. A drought might affect a region by causing crops to die and people to go hungry.
3. As a consequence of contracting a virus, a person is likely to become ill.
4. If warning nations call for a truce, a period of peace is likely to occur.
5. I might alter the route I take to school if I move to a new neighborhood.

Build Language Skills: Grammar, p. 79

A. 1. The family consisted of a couple, their married children, and their grandchildren.
2. Aztec houses were very plain; everyone slept on mats of reeds.

B. Guidelines for evaluation: Students should write two grammatically correct sentences about the Aztecs. In one they should use one or more commas in one of the ways described in the lesson, and in the other they should use one or more semicolons in one of the ways described in the lesson.

"Popocatepetl and Ixtlaccihuatl"
by Juliet Piggott Wood

Selection Test A, p. 80

Critical Reading

1. ANS: D	DIF: Easy	OBJ: Comprehension
2. ANS: B	DIF: Easy	OBJ: Interpretation
3. ANS: C	DIF: Easy	OBJ: Reading
4. ANS: C	DIF: Easy	OBJ: Reading
5. ANS: D	DIF: Easy	OBJ: Comprehension
6. ANS: B	DIF: Easy	OBJ: Comprehension
7. ANS: D	DIF: Easy	OBJ: Reading
8. ANS: A	DIF: Easy	OBJ: Literary Analysis

9. ANS: A	DIF: Easy	OBJ: Interpretation
10. ANS: B	DIF: Easy	OBJ: Literary Analysis
11. ANS: C	DIF: Easy	OBJ: Interpretation

Vocabulary and Grammar

12. ANS: B	DIF: Easy	OBJ: Vocabulary
13. ANS: A	DIF: Easy	OBJ: Grammar
14. ANS: B	DIF: Easy	OBJ: Grammar

Essay

15. Students will most likely note that Ixtla and Popo are well suited to each other. They should focus on the characters' fierce loyalty to each other and to the Emperor (though they are in love and want to marry, they honor his wishes that they not marry).

Difficulty: *Easy*

Objective: *Essay*

16. Students should support their response with a well-reasoned explanation. They may hold that the warriors got the fate they deserved since they had acted selfishly and without regard for human life. Alternatively, students may suggest that the warriors could not have known their lies would lead to Ixtla's death and may regard Popo's behavior as excessive, in which case they might suggest that the warriors could have been exiled or imprisoned instead of killed.

Difficulty: *Easy*

Objective: *Essay*

Selection Test B, p. 83

Critical Reading

1. ANS: A	DIF: Average	OBJ: Comprehension
2. ANS: C	DIF: Average	OBJ: Comprehension
3. ANS: A	DIF: Average	OBJ: Interpretation
4. ANS: B	DIF: Average	OBJ: Interpretation
5. ANS: D	DIF: Average	OBJ: Comprehension
6. ANS: D	DIF: Average	OBJ: Reading
7. ANS: C	DIF: Average	OBJ: Comprehension
8. ANS: B	DIF: Average	OBJ: Reading
9. ANS: B	DIF: Challenging	OBJ: Interpretation
10. ANS: C	DIF: Average	OBJ: Interpretation
11. ANS: B	DIF: Challenging	OBJ: Interpretation
12. ANS: C	DIF: Average	OBJ: Interpretation
13. ANS: C	DIF: Challenging	OBJ: Interpretation
14. ANS: A	DIF: Average	OBJ: Literary Analysis
15. ANS: B	DIF: Average	OBJ: Literary Analysis

Vocabulary and Grammar

| 16. ANS: C | DIF: Average | OBJ: Vocabulary |
| 17. ANS: A | DIF: Challenging | OBJ: Vocabulary |

| 18. ANS: B | DIF: Challenging | OBJ: Grammar |
| 19. ANS: A | DIF: Average | OBJ: Grammar |

Essay

20. Students should recognize that Ixtla is given an education and expected to succeed her father as ruler of the state but is not free to marry or choose the man she will marry.

Difficulty: *Average*

Objective: *Essay*

21. Students may mention studiousness, seriousness, obedience, loyalty, courage, and strength in battle, honesty, and "true" wisdom and should cite details from the legend to support their claims.

Difficulty: *Average*

Objective: *Essay*

22. Students may point to such universal elements as the idealized love between Popo and Ixtla, the protracted war between the Emperor and his opponents, Popo's success at proving himself the best warrior of all, the other warriors' jealousy, and the tragedy that leads to Ixtla's death.

Difficulty: *Challenging*

Objective: *Essay*

"Perseus" by Alice Low
"Percy-Us Brings the Gawgon's Head" by Lloyd Alexander

Vocabulary Warm-up Exercises, p. 87

A. 1. slay
2. horrible
3. Fortunately
4. marble
5. glittering
6. sandals
7. invisible
8. hideous

B. Sample Answers

1. Dean took a shower; <u>afterward</u>, he dried off, using a big, white towel.
2. You can tell that Candace is <u>confident</u> because she stands up straight.
3. The nervous cat, <u>hissing</u> at the dog, was obviously angry and tense.
4. The <u>petrified</u> trees were as hard as rocks.
5. Carly and Josie <u>regret</u> that they did not study enough for the exam.
6. Because the <u>serpents</u> were near, the mice were in danger.
7. As a <u>spectator</u> at the football game, Matt wore a jacket and a muffler.

Reading Warm-up A, p. 88

Sample Answers

1. (on his feet); Patricia bought a new pair of *sandals* for the summer.
2. <u>No one could see him</u>; An *invisible* force that affects me in everyday life is gravity.
3. (jewelry); *Glittering* means "sparkling."
4. <u>statue</u>; Three other materials besides *marble* that might be used for a statue are bronze, granite, and wood.
5. <u>sea monster</u>; A jacket described as *hideous* might be made of very brightly colored fabric and have lots of metal ornaments on it.
6. (I can save you!); Another word that means about the same as *fortunately* is *luckily*.
7. (kill); The heroes *slay* the monsters.
8. (roaring loudly); *Horrible* means "frightful" or "causing horror."

Reading Warm-up B, p. 89

Sample Answers

1. <u>hair</u>; Another word that means the same as *serpents* is *snakes*.
2. (looked at them); I was a *spectator* at a soccer game on Saturday.
3. <u>statue</u>; Carlos has a collection of *petrified* wood.
4. (snakes); *Hissing* means "making a prolonged sound like ss."
5. <u>Medusa lived in a cavern with her two sisters</u>; On Sunday, my friend Marsha and I skated at the ice-skating rink. *Afterward*, we had hot chocolate.
6. (frightening); The circus act was *utterly* amazing.
7. <u>her own beauty</u>; I feel *confident* about my talent as a guitarist.
8. (that she had dared to compare herself to a goddess); One thing that I *regret* is being mean to my little sister.

Literary Analysis: Comparing Treatment of Epic Conventions, p. 90

1. *"Perseus"*: in Argos, on the sea, on an unnamed island, in "the gray land," in the north, on the island of the Gorgons, back on the unnamed island, and back in Argos; *"Percy-Us"*: in an unnamed location, in the air, in the mountain range and cave where The Gawgon lives, and in the palace of Polly Deck-Tease
2. *"Perseus"*: Perseus; *"Percy-Us"*: Percy-Us
3. *"Perseus"*: Danaë, a princess, and Zeus, a god; *"Percy-Us"*: information not mentioned
4. *"Perseus"*: Perseus must bring Polydectes the head of the Gorgon Medusa; *"Percy-Us"*: Percy-Us must bring Polly Deck-Tease the head of The Gawgon.
5. *"Perseus"*: Hermes and Athena; *"Percy-Us"*: Hermes and The Gawgon

6. *"Perseus"*: Medusa is huge and hideous, has wings, and has hair made of snakes; *"Percy-Us"*: The Gawgon has snakes for hair but otherwise seems like a human being: she sits in a rocking chair and carries on a helpful, friendly conversation with Percy-Us.
7. *"Perseus"*: Perseus slays Medusa, brings the head back to Polydectes, and when he realizes that Polydectes had meant for him to die, shows the head to him, turning him to stone; *"Percy-Us"*: Percy-Us strikes a deal with The Gawgon, brings her back alive, and, after Polly Deck-Tease taunts him, has The Gawgon turn Polly Deck-Tease and his guests to stone.
8. *"Perseus"*: probably like the original epic; *"Percy-Us"*: a humorous retelling of the epic.

Vocabulary Builder, p. 91

A. Sample Answers

1. The sentence does not make sense because no one would admire a hideous dress. *New sentence:* Everyone looked away from the hideous dress.
2. The sentence makes sense because trees in a petrified forest have turned into stone.
3. The sentence does not make sense because the children cannot be pursuing their mother while waiting for her. *New sentence:* The children were in *pursuit* of their mother, following her down the aisles of the huge supermarket.
4. The sentence makes sense because dogs are often afraid during thunderstorms.

B. 1. D; 2. A; 3. C

Selection Test A, p. 93

Critical Reading

1. ANS: B	DIF: Easy	OBJ: Comprehension
2. ANS: C	DIF: Easy	OBJ: Comprehension
3. ANS: A	DIF: Easy	OBJ: Comprehension
4. ANS: D	DIF: Easy	OBJ: Interpretation
5. ANS: B	DIF: Easy	OBJ: Comprehension
6. ANS: C	DIF: Easy	OBJ: Comprehension
7. ANS: B	DIF: Easy	OBJ: Interpretation
8. ANS: A	DIF: Easy	OBJ: Interpretation
9. ANS: C	DIF: Easy	OBJ: Literary Analysis
10. ANS: A	DIF: Easy	OBJ: Literary Analysis
11. ANS: D	DIF: Easy	OBJ: Literary Analysis
12. ANS: A	DIF: Easy	OBJ: Literary Analysis

Vocabulary

13. ANS: D	DIF: Easy	OBJ: Vocabulary
14. ANS: A	DIF: Easy	OBJ: Vocabulary
15. ANS: B	DIF: Easy	OBJ: Vocabulary

Essay

16. Students should clearly describe the two scenes: In the first instance, Perseus is advised by Athena to strike while the Gorgon sleeps; he looks into the shield and cuts off the head with one blow. In the second instance, Percy-Us finds The Gawgon waiting for him. She invites him to cut off her head and encourages him to try again when he misses because he is confused by the mirror image. At last she convinces him to take her alive to Polly Deck-Tease, so she saves her life while Percy-Us still fulfills his promise. Students should present a valid reason for finding one or the other character more successful.

    Difficulty: *Easy*

    Objective: *Essay*

17. Students should note that the monsters are alike only in that both have snakes for hair and are supposed to turn to stone anyone who looks at them. Students should note that Medusa is a huge, hideous winged creature, whereas The Gawgon appears to be more like a human—she sits on a rocking chair and carries on a seemingly normal conversation. Students may also point out that The Gawgon does not turn everyone to stone—she instructs Percy-Us to eat a licorice gumdrop, and after he does, he can look at her and live.

    Difficulty: *Easy*

    Objective: *Essay*

Selection Test B, p. 96

Critical Reading

1. ANS: B	DIF: Average	OBJ: Comprehension
2. ANS: C	DIF: Average	OBJ: Interpretation
3. ANS: A	DIF: Challenging	OBJ: Comprehension
4. ANS: B	DIF: Average	OBJ: Comprehension
5. ANS: D	DIF: Average	OBJ: Comprehension
6. ANS: A	DIF: Average	OBJ: Interpretation
7. ANS: D	DIF: Average	OBJ: Interpretation
8. ANS: C	DIF: Average	OBJ: Literary Analysis
9. ANS: A	DIF: Average	OBJ: Literary Analysis
10. ANS: B	DIF: Average	OBJ: Literary Analysis
11. ANS: D	DIF: Average	OBJ: Literary Analysis
12. ANS: A	DIF: Challenging	OBJ: Literary Analysis
13. ANS: B	DIF: Average	OBJ: Literary Analysis

Vocabulary

14. ANS: C	DIF: Challenging	OBJ: Vocabulary
15. ANS: A	DIF: Average	OBJ: Vocabulary

16. ANS: D	DIF: Challenging	OBJ: Vocabulary
17. ANS: C	DIF: Average	OBJ: Vocabulary

Essay

18. Students should note that both heroes must fulfill the same quest and that both heroes receive some help. Students should note at least two of the following differences: Perseus reaches the Gorgons' home without trouble; Percy-Us has difficulties flying. Perseus finds the three Gorgons sleeping and cuts off Medusa's head on his first attempt; Percy-Us finds only one creature, The Gawgon; she is awake and waiting for him, and he is unsuccessful in several attempts to cut off her head. Perseus returns to Polydectes, is taunted by him, and in retaliation, shows him the head, causing Polydectes to turn to stone. Percy-Us is convinced by the Gawgon to allow her to live. Percy-Us is not taunted by Polly Deck-Tease, but Polly Deck-Tease and all his guests are turned to stone when The Gawgon presents herself. Perseus goes on to marry and then cause his father's death, whereas Percy-Us's story ends with the death of Polly Deck-Tease. Students should support their opinions of whether one character is more heroic with at least one detail from the selection whose hero they find more "heroic."

    Difficulty: *Average*

    Objective: *Essay*

19. Students should recognize that all of the characteristics are present in "Perseus." The first three are present in "Percy-Us," but the style of "Percy-Us" is of course not serious and formal. They should suggest a sound reason to support their opinion of whether "Percy-Us" may still be considered an epic.

    Difficulty: *Challenging*

    Objective: *Essay*

Writing Workshop—Unit 6, Part 1

Business Letter: Integrating Grammar Skills, p. 100

A. 1. A; 2. A; 3. B

B. After the federal government cut money to the states, most state, county, and local governments had budget problems. Many libraries and other local services had to be cut back. Hoping to help, a group of people began Bookworms, an organization that is raising funds for the local library. One of the first things Bookworms organized was an art show. Many creative, talented artists donated their works, and the money from the sales went to the library.

Unit 6, Part 1 Answers

Benchmark Test 11, p. 101

MULTIPLE CHOICE

1. ANS: A
2. ANS: C
3. ANS: D
4. ANS: C
5. ANS: D
6. ANS: B
7. ANS: D
8. ANS: B
9. ANS: A
10. ANS: C
11. ANS: B
12. ANS: D
13. ANS: C
14. ANS: D
15. ANS: A
16. ANS: C
17. ANS: D
18. ANS: A
19. ANS: C
20. ANS: A
21. ANS: B
22. ANS: A
23. ANS: B
24. ANS: A
25. ANS: C
26. ANS: B
27. ANS: D
28. ANS: D
29. ANS: A
30. ANS: B
31. ANS: D
32. ANS: C
33. ANS: D

ESSAY

34. Students should indicate the action of the myth by identifying a problem or conflict and its solution or resolution. They should also indicate characters in the myth and the traits characters will display. They should indicate time of day and may also provide other setting details.

35. Students should clearly identify the place they are describing and the source from which it comes if it is not of their own invention. They should include in their descriptions details about the time and place as well as the overall environment or atmosphere of the place they describe. They should use vivid verbs and adjectives to make the description interesting.

36. Students should use either block or modified block format and should include a heading (with date), inside address, greeting, body, closing, and signature. They should clearly state their complaint about the product and give details supporting that complaint. They should use formal and polite language. They may suggest how a refund should be handled and include a question about whether or not they should return the product, and to where.

Unit 6, Part 2 Answers

Diagnostic Test 12, p. 108

MULTIPLE CHOICE

1. ANS: C
2. ANS: B
3. ANS: A
4. ANS: D
5. ANS: B
6. ANS: B
7. ANS: D
8. ANS: B
9. ANS: D
10. ANS: B
11. ANS: A
12. ANS: B
13. ANS: C
14. ANS: C
15. ANS: B

"Sun and Moon in a Box"
by Richard Erdoes and Alfonso Ortiz

Vocabulary Warm-up Exercises, p. 112

A.
1. eagle
2. cunning
3. reliable
4. relented
5. talons
6. wooded
7. burden
8. lag

B. Sample Answers
1. The *grasshoppers* could jump very far with their powerful hind legs.
2. If we lie and *betray* our friends, they will learn they cannot *rely* on us.

3. It is not very pleasant when someone is continuously *pestering* us.

4. The *outer* layer of clothing is the easiest one to remove if you are too warm.

5. The majority of voters *objected* to the proposed law, so it did not pass.

6. Because Tom *regretted* his rudeness, he decided to apologize.

Reading Warm-up A, p. 113

Sample Answers

1. (after a lot of pleading on my part); *Relented* means "became less stubborn."

2. The camp; A waterfall or hiking trails might be located in a *wooded* area.

3. (atop the cliffs); An *eagle* is "a large bird of the hawk family."

4. predator; Synonyms for *cunning* are *skillful* or *clever.*

5. The eagle will swoop at the slower bird., The eagle quickly grasps the prey in its sharp talons and flies away.; Emily did not sleep well the night before, and so she started to *lag* behind in the race.

6. (the prey); Other animals with *talons* are hawks and dinosaurs.

7. (The prey it carries in its claws); *Burden* means "a load that is carried."

8. who always bring food back to the nest for the hungry chicks; The *reliable* crossing guard was always at her station each morning.

Reading Warm-up B, p. 114

Sample Answers

1. The outer rooms housed the families.; *Outer* means "located farther out than another spot or place."

2. (The families were used to living together); A synonym for *embarrassed* is *flustered.*

3. (invaders); Spies who sell their country's secrets *betray* their nation.

4. If children wanted to join in the work; I have *objected* to people who do not pick up their litter.

5. The children's questions; A synonym for *pestering* is *bothering.*

6. (on being able to pass traditional skills on to the younger generation); May I *rely* on you to walk the dog for me tonight?

7. During the years, unfortunately, some traditional skills and cultural activities faded away, as European practices took their place.; I have *regretted* not taking better care of my garden.

8. stones and minerals; *Grasshoppers* are "insects that leap and eat plants and have powerful hind legs."

"Sun and Moon in a Box"
by Richard Erdoes and Alfonso Ortiz

Reading: Use Prior Knowledge to Compare and Contrast, p. 115

Sample Answers

2. *Question:* Are the Kachinas like anything I have read about? Are they like the gods and goddesses in Greek myths? *Comparison/Contrast:* The Kachinas do not talk or interact with the Eagle and the Coyote. They seem more spiritual and more connected to nature than the Greek gods and goddesses.

3. *Question:* Is this box going to turn out to be like Pandora's box? *Comparison/Contrast:* Like Coyote, Pandora gets a box and is told not to open it. Like Coyote, Pandora is curious.

4. *Question:* What is the difference between what happens when Coyote opens his box and what happens when Pandora opens hers? *Comparison/Contrast:* When Coyote opens his box, winter comes to the Earth. When Pandora opens hers, all the troubles of the world are released.

Literary Analysis: Cultural Context, p. 116

1. place; The references to "the west" and "a deep canyon" indicate that the folk tale is set in the American Southwest.

2. beliefs; The passage suggests that the Zuni believed that, at a much earlier time, the Kachinas controlled the sun and the moon. They treated them as if they were precious, using each one only a little at a time.

3. beliefs; The passage suggests that the Zuni believed that borrowing was acceptable but stealing was not.

4. customs *or* beliefs; The passage suggests that the Zuni helped each other with hard work; perhaps they believed it was embarrassing to be seen letting someone else do all the work.

Vocabulary Builder, p. 117

A. Sample Answers

1. Tyler was likely to return the book because he is dependable.

2. The parents gave in, so we know that the family kept the dog.

3. She was not able to keep herself from planning, so she clearly could not curb her excitement.

B. 1. F; *Reliable* means "dependable," and a car that starts only half the time is not dependable.

2. F; *Relented* means "gave in," and someone who refuses to give in to someone else's pleas has not relented.

3. T; *Curb* means "control," and someone who can keep a secret is able to control the urge to tell a best friend everything.

Enrichment: Coyote, the Character With Many Roles, p. 120

Sample Answers

1. Coyote does not play the role of a hero. He is not part human, and he does not help any humans. (There are no humans in the story, in fact.)

2. Coyote does play the role of a trickster. He tricks Eagle into letting him have the box, and then he runs off with it. He also is a survivor. Nothing serious happens as a result of his actions. He only has to listen to Eagle criticize him.

3. Coyote plays the role of a fool. He is foolish and greedy when he steals the box, and he is very foolish when he opens it.

4. Coyote teaches at least two lessons: Do not steal, and do not interfere with the harmony of the natural world.

Selection Test A, p. 121

Critical Reading

1. ANS: A	DIF: Easy	OBJ: Literary Analysis
2. ANS: C	DIF: Easy	OBJ: Comprehension
3. ANS: C	DIF: Easy	OBJ: Interpretation
4. ANS: B	DIF: Easy	OBJ: Comprehension
5. ANS: C	DIF: Easy	OBJ: Reading
6. ANS: C	DIF: Easy	OBJ: Reading
7. ANS: C	DIF: Easy	OBJ: Interpretation
8. ANS: A	DIF: Easy	OBJ: Interpretation
9. ANS: C	DIF: Easy	OBJ: Comprehension
10. ANS: A	DIF: Easy	OBJ: Interpretation
11. ANS: C	DIF: Easy	OBJ: Interpretation
12. ANS: B	DIF: Easy	OBJ: Literary Analysis
13. ANS: B	DIF: Easy	OBJ: Literary Analysis

Vocabulary and Grammar

14. ANS: C	DIF: Easy	OBJ: Vocabulary
15. ANS: C	DIF: Easy	OBJ: Grammar

Essay

16. Students who think that Eagle should not have allowed Coyote to carry the box may cite the line in which Coyote suggests that they steal it. That statement strongly suggests that Coyote is not trustworthy. Students who agree with Eagle's decision to let Coyote carry the box may point to the animals' friendship or to Eagle's compassion for Coyote's claims that he will lose the respect of his family if he does not carry it; they may say that it is a virtue to trust one's fellow creatures.

Difficulty: *Easy*

Objective: *Essay*

17. Students may point out these similarities: Both are creatures, both are hunters, both are drawn to the box and its contents. They may point out these differences:

Eagle is a bird; he travels by flying; Coyote is an animal; he travels by running and, when he has to, swimming. Coyote hunts grasshoppers; Eagle hunts rabbits. Coyote wants to steal the box containing the sun and the moon; Eagle wants only to borrow it. Eagle is reliable; Coyote is cunning and unreliable.

Difficulty: *Easy*

Objective: *Essay*

Selection Test B, p. 124

Critical Reading

1. ANS: D	DIF: Average	OBJ: Literary Analysis
2. ANS: C	DIF: Average	OBJ: Comprehension
3. ANS: A	DIF: Average	OBJ: Comprehension
4. ANS: B	DIF: Challenging	OBJ: Interpretation
5. ANS: D	DIF: Challenging	OBJ: Literary Analysis
6. ANS: C	DIF: Average	OBJ: Interpretation
7. ANS: A	DIF: Average	OBJ: Interpretation
8. ANS: B	DIF: Average	OBJ: Interpretation
9. ANS: D	DIF: Average	OBJ: Interpretation
10. ANS: B	DIF: Challenging	OBJ: Reading
11. ANS: C	DIF: Average	OBJ: Reading
12. ANS: C	DIF: Average	OBJ: Literary Analysis
13. ANS: B	DIF: Average	OBJ: Literary Analysis
14. ANS: C	DIF: Challenging	OBJ: Literary Analysis

Vocabulary and Grammar

15. ANS: A	DIF: Average	OBJ: Vocabulary
16. ANS: C	DIF: Average	OBJ: Vocabulary
17. ANS: D	DIF: Average	OBJ: Grammar
18. ANS: C	DIF: Average	OBJ: Grammar

Essay

19. Students who hold that Eagle shares in the responsibility should point out that Eagle takes the box in the first place and admits to knowing that Coyote is not reliable. Students who hold that Eagle is not responsible may point out that he meant only to borrow the box and that he is motivated by compassion—by the pity he feels for the arguments Coyote raises—to let Coyote carry the box for a while.

Difficulty: *Average*

Objective: *Essay*

20. Students should recognize that Coyote is deceitful, greedy, and uncontrollably curious, whereas Eagle is moderate and reliable. They should point out that Eagle's traits are undoubtedly ones the Zuni valued, whereas Coyote's traits are ones seen as undesirable.

Difficulty: *Challenging*

Objective: *Essay*

"How the Snake Got Poison"
by Zora Neale Hurston

Vocabulary Warm-up Exercises, p. 128

A. 1. fight
2. enemy
3. claws
4. snakes
5. belly
6. poison
7. shakes
8. rattles

B. Sample Answers
1. vastness; The scope and <u>vastness</u> of the history book are very great.
2. world; We must take care of our <u>world</u> if we want it to survive.
3. decorate; We will <u>decorate</u> the house with flowers for the party.
4. defense; Our <u>defense</u> against burglars is a watch dog.
5. stamped; We <u>stamped</u> out the embers so a fire would not start.
6. relations; Past <u>relations</u> in our family fought in the Civil War.
7. topic; The <u>topic</u> of her term paper is the history of women's suffrage.

Reading Warm-up A, p. 129

Sample Answers
1. (reptiles that have no legs); A few kinds of *snakes* are cobras, garter snakes, and copperheads.
2. (a snake moves along the ground) (Some snakes also use these muscles for climbing trees.); *Belly* means "the stomach or underside of an animal."
3. <u>deadly</u>; Some frogs have *poison* in their skin, which protects them from animals that might eat them.
4. (mountain lions or bears); Other animals that have *claws* are lizards, cats, dogs, and raccoons.
5. <u>rattlesnake</u>; *Fight* means "to take part in a physical struggle or battle."
6. (the series of rings called rattles that grow on its tail); Someone who *shakes* out a rug is usually trying to get the dirt out of it.
7. <u>on its tail</u>; *Rattles* are "rings on a rattlesnake's tail that make a rattling sound."
8. <u>the animals they like to eat. Such prey includes toads, lizards, mice, and birds</u>; *Enemy* means "a foe."

Reading Warm-up B, p. 130

Sample Answers
1. <u>kinds of plants and animals</u>; *Earth* means "this world or the planet we live on."
2. (The growing grass and the graceful antelopes); I would *ornament* my room with posters and pictures of friends and family.
3. (the world's many habitats); An antonym for *immensity* is *smallness*.
4. <u>The immensity of the world's many habitats</u>; I wonder about the *subject* of how to predict earthquakes.
5. <u>a colony of termites</u>; *Stomped* means "to have injured or killed by stamping on or out."
6. (whales could not exist); I hope that future *generations* of my family will inherit a healthy planet earth.
7. (educating others about the importance of the balance of nature); I am working *towards* getting along better with my brothers.
8. <u>by preserving the entire habitat in which it lives</u>; What kind of *protection* will we give to the more delicate plants in the garden during winter?

"How the Snake Got Poison"
by Zora Neale Hurston

Reading: Use Prior Knowledge to Compare and Contrast, p. 131

Note: For students to write answers such as these, they would have to have some prior knowledge of snakes or have done some basic research.

Sample Answers
2. *Question:* How are snakes portrayed in Greek mythology? *Comparison/Contrast:* In Greek mythology, the snake was sacred to medicine. That is why a staff with a snake coiled around it symbolizes medicine.
3. *Question:* How is this snake's behavior like that of the poisonous snakes described in the story "Rattlesnake Hunt"? *Comparison/Contrast:* Those snakes are active only when the weather is warm. Some of them live in gopher holes and will not come out unless they are disturbed.
4. *Question:* How does this solution compare with the way the rattlesnake uses its rattle in real life? *Comparison/Contrast:* I read that not all rattlesnakes use the rattle before they strike.

Literary Analysis: Cultural Context, p. 132

Sample Answers

1. The passage suggests that the African Americans who told this tale believed that all creatures have the right to protect themselves. Possibly the passage has a broader meaning: that all people must be able to protect themselves.

2. The passage suggests that the African Americans who told this tale believed that every creature should be allowed to protect itself but that it is wrong to kill every creature without regard to who it is or without first considering whether there is a need to kill.

3. The passage suggests that the African Americans who told this tale believed that friends should be protected from harm, but enemies deserve their fate.

Vocabulary Builder, p. 133

A. Sample Answers

1. *Ornament* means "decorate," so the garbage cans would not ornament the property; they would be ugly.

2. An immensity is an immeasurably large space, so a condor would not be able to survive in a small space.

B. 1. T; *Ornament* means "beautify," and those items would make a backyard beautiful.

2. F; *Immensity* is an immeasurably large space, so it could not easily be fenced in.

C. 1. C; 2. D

Enrichment: Snakes Are Not So Bad, p. 136

1. Most snakes avoid humans whenever they can and strike only when they are cornered or harassed.

2. Snakes are an important part of the food chain. They kill rats and mice that eat crops. They also are fed on by hawks, mongooses, and bigger snakes.

3. Snakes are dry and scaly, not slimy.

"Sun and Moon in a Box"
by Richard Erdoes and Alfonso Ortiz
"How the Snake Got Poison"
by Zora Neale Hurston

Build Language Skills: Vocabulary, p. 137

Sample Answers

A. 1. The rudeness of the person who bumped into me in the mall was so extreme that I was angry for the next hour.

2. Anthony was completely honest about his desire to win the science-fair competition.

B. 1. Scientists analyze the results of an experiment to figure out what they mean.

2. One aspect of snakes I would research is how they survive in cold weather.

3. In "Sun and Moon in a Box," I liked the detail of the setting, where Earth is described as "still soft and new."

4. A unique characteristic of a snake is its ability to shed its skin.

Build Language Skills: Grammar, p. 138

A. 1. The character named Coyote suggested that they steal the box.

2. The folk tale takes place in the American Southwest, perhaps in present-day Arizona or New Mexico.

3. Coyote said to Eagle, "This is a wonderful thing."

4. "I do not trust you," Eagle said many times. "You will open that box."

B. Students' episodes should describe Coyote's actions after he opens the box containing the sun and the moon. Writing should be grammatically correct and should include at least one quotation, one proper noun, and one proper adjective, all correctly capitalized.

"How the Snake Got Poison"
by Zora Neale Hurston

Selection Test A, p. 139

Critical Reading

1. ANS: B	DIF: Easy	OBJ: Literary Analysis
2. ANS: B	DIF: Easy	OBJ: Comprehension
3. ANS: C	DIF: Easy	OBJ: Interpretation
4. ANS: A	DIF: Easy	OBJ: Reading
5. ANS: C	DIF: Easy	OBJ: Comprehension
6. ANS: A	DIF: Easy	OBJ: Comprehension
7. ANS: A	DIF: Easy	OBJ: Reading
8. ANS: D	DIF: Easy	OBJ: Comprehension
9. ANS: D	DIF: Easy	OBJ: Comprehension
10. ANS: C	DIF: Easy	OBJ: Interpretation
11. ANS: A	DIF: Easy	OBJ: Literary Analysis
12. ANS: B	DIF: Easy	OBJ: Interpretation

Vocabulary and Grammar

13. ANS: B	DIF: Easy	OBJ: Vocabulary
14. ANS: D	DIF: Easy	OBJ: Grammar
15. ANS: C	DIF: Easy	OBJ: Grammar

Essay

16. Students who find the snake sneaky may suggest that it might have gotten along without the poison—there are many nonpoisonous snakes—or that it might not have attacked every creature that approached. Students who say the snake was not sneaky will likely argue that its

complaints were reasonable. Students should express their opinion of the snake's character and defend it with a reference to at least one detail from the selection.

Difficulty: *Easy*

Objective: *Essay*

17. Students may note that the informal style adds humor to the story and that the dialect makes the cultural context especially vivid, or they may object to those characteristics, saying that they detract from the message of the folk tale. Students should state their opinion of the effect of the dialect and informal style on the selection's overall effect and cite two examples to support their ideas.

Difficulty: *Easy*

Objective: *Essay*

Selection Test B, p. 142

Critical Reading

1. ANS: B	DIF: Average	OBJ: Comprehension
2. ANS: C	DIF: Average	OBJ: Comprehension
3. ANS: A	DIF: Average	OBJ: Comprehension
4. ANS: B	DIF: Challenging	OBJ: Interpretation
5. ANS: B	DIF: Average	OBJ: Literary Analysis
6. ANS: D	DIF: Challenging	OBJ: Interpretation
7. ANS: D	DIF: Challenging	OBJ: Reading
8. ANS: C	DIF: Challenging	OBJ: Reading
9. ANS: A	DIF: Challenging	OBJ: Reading
10. ANS: C	DIF: Average	OBJ: Interpretation
11. ANS: D	DIF: Challenging	OBJ: Interpretation
12. ANS: D	DIF: Average	OBJ: Comprehension
13. ANS: A	DIF: Challenging	OBJ: Literary Analysis
14. ANS: C	DIF: Average	OBJ: Literary Analysis
15. ANS: B	DIF: Challenging	OBJ: Interpretation

Vocabulary and Grammar

16. ANS: B	DIF: Average	OBJ: Vocabulary
17. ANS: A	DIF: Average	OBJ: Vocabulary
18. ANS: C	DIF: Average	OBJ: Grammar

Essay

19. Students are likely to say that each argument is valid. Although the animals seem to be bickering, there is a sense that God solved the problem with the rattle, and that resolution suggests that the animals were not arguing for the sake of arguing—had they been, the rattle would not have solved the problem. Students may suggest alternative solutions or express satisfaction with the one described in the selection.

Difficulty: *Average*

Objective: *Essay*

20. Students will likely recognize the tendency of people to defer to a third party rather than confront an adversary. They might mention the role that courts and labor mediators play in settling disputes.

Difficulty: *Challenging*

Objective: *Essay*

21. Students should recognize that nature is out of balance because the snake has no natural means of defense. God's statement expresses the belief that every creature must be able to defend itself. Students may point out that God's first solution does not correct the balance— the other creatures are unable to defend themselves against the snake's poison. At last, God provides the snake with the rattle, and then the balance of nature is maintained.

Difficulty: *Challenging*

Objective: *Essay*

"The People Could Fly" by Virginia Hamilton

Vocabulary Warm-up Exercises, p. 146

A. 1. plantation
2. horseback
3. labored
4. flock
5. firelight
6. hip
7. babe
8. soothe

B. Sample Answers

1. T; If one is very familiar with *African* folk tales, one probably knows a lot about Africa because *African* describes anything having to do with Africa.

2. F; *Clumsily* means Carol moves "awkwardly or ungracefully," which means she probably does not have the coordination to ice skate well.

3. T; *Bled* means he "was bleeding" and that is very likely if he cut himself.

4. F; *Misery* means "unhappiness," so the expression "misery loves company" means one wants others to feel unhappy, too.

5. T; *Souls* means "people," so if there were a lot of souls at the meeting, it means a lot of people were there.

6. F; *Sundown* is when the sun is setting at the end of the day, so one would not be waking up early at that time.

7. T; *Bawling* means "crying or wailing loudly," so if someone if crying she or he is not very happy.

8. T; *Slavery* means owning people as property and using the slaves as workers.

Reading Warm-up A, p. 147

Sample Answers

1. (cotton); *Plantation* means "a farm or estate, sometimes cultivated by the workers who live there."

2. (she was not given enough time to care for me. Instead, she was sent back to the fields to work. The night was her favorite time, for then we were together again.); My mother said that when I was a *babe* I slept during the day instead of during the night.

3. the glow and warmth; I like how the *firelight* makes the room seem so cozy.

4. (I remember how my mother sometimes carried her in a sort of hip cloth tied to her body like a sling.); *Hip* means "located by someone's hip bone at the top of the leg."

5. Being carried that way; Listening to soft music or going on a walk can *soothe* me.

6. (The overseer); People who ride on *horseback* often know how to make their horses trot and gallop.

7. Like a flock of birds or animals; A *flock* is "a large group of animals, people, or things that are found together."

8. Picking cotton was hard, hot work. It cut our hands; Sometimes we sang songs to keep our spirits alive.; I have *labored* at finishing my homework assignment on time.

Reading Warm-up B, p. 148

Sample Answers

1. large numbers of African people were captured by slave traders; The slaves brought their *African* heritage with them.

2. (were shipped like cargo, under terrible conditions. They were taken to the West Indies and to the Americas to be sold into slavery.); *Souls* means "people."

3. (Slave traders realized there was a great need for cheap labor in the West Indian and British colonies. They saw the taking of Africans as a way to fill this need and to profit by it.); *Slavery* is wrong because it is against the law and it is a bad way to treat other human beings; it treats a person as a piece of property and takes away his or her freedom, which is that person's right.

4. The captives' freedom and their culture were savagely stripped away from them; they realized they would never see another sunrise or sundown as a free man or woman; *Misery* means "sorrow or discomfort."

5. The *sundown* takes place at dusk every day, so they realized that as slaves, every day, they would experience bondage, and the sunrises and sundowns would never be the same for them as when they were free.

6. (They were mercilessly chained together, causing them to move clumsily.); Yes, I have moved *clumsily* when I took part in a three-legged sack race.

7. Those who rebelled were beaten or whipped until they bled; The puppy bled when it cut its paw on a piece of glass.

8. (Unsanitary conditions and lack of food caused much illness, and the bawling of the agonized captives could be heard.); *Bawling* means "noisy crying or wailing."

"The People Could Fly" by Virginia Hamilton

Reading: Use a Venn Diagram to Compare and Contrast, p. 149

1. *Toby:* is old, has no family, has learned to survive oppression, still remembers the magic words; *Both:* are descended from Africans, are enslaved, can fly; *Sarah:* is young, has a child, is being destroyed by oppression, no longer remembers the magic words

2. *Enslaved People:* are descended from Africans, are forced to work, may be whipped, are not free; *Both:* are human beings, work for the so-called master; *Overseer and Driver:* are descended from Europeans, choose to work, force the enslaved people to work, are free

Literary Analysis: Folk Tale, p. 150

Sample Answers

1. The passage clearly presents evil. The people have been enslaved, and they are miserable.

2. The passage clearly presents evil. The Driver is cruelly whipping the people and causing them terrible pain.

3. The passage presents a clear distinction between good and evil. The woman has been hurt by the evil Driver. Toby represents good.

4. The passage presents a clear distinction between good and evil. Again the Driver represents evil, and Toby represents good.

5. This passage teaches a lesson about life. It suggests that you have to wait your turn, and when your turn comes, you must take it.

6. The passage teaches a lesson about life. It teaches that it is important to keep your heritage by teaching your children about the past.

Vocabulary Builder, p. 151

A. Sample Answers

1. The workers were right to protest because they were being treated badly; they were being looked down on.

2. The singer will sing a soft, soothing song.

3. The clowns are walking slowly and dragging their feet.

B. Sample answers follow each true or false designation:

1. F; A teacher who is well loved would not also be looked down on.

2. T; A love song is likely to be sung in a quiet, soothing manner.

3. F; A person taking a power walk is not likely to drag his or her feet.

C. 1. C; 2. D; 3. A

Enrichment: Oral Tradition, p. 154

Students should commit to memory at least the story line and main ideas of a short, simple folk tale and be able to present it to a small audience.

Selection Test A, p. 155

Critical Reading

1. ANS: A	DIF: Easy	OBJ: Comprehension
2. ANS: B	DIF: Easy	OBJ: Comprehension
3. ANS: C	DIF: Easy	OBJ: Interpretation
4. ANS: D	DIF: Easy	OBJ: Comprehension
5. ANS: B	DIF: Easy	OBJ: Reading
6. ANS: B	DIF: Easy	OBJ: Comprehension
7. ANS: A	DIF: Easy	OBJ: Literary Analysis
8. ANS: C	DIF: Easy	OBJ: Reading
9. ANS: D	DIF: Easy	OBJ: Interpretation
10. ANS: C	DIF: Easy	OBJ: Interpretation
11. ANS: D	DIF: Easy	OBJ: Literary Analysis
12. ANS: C	DIF: Easy	OBJ: Literary Analysis
13. ANS: A	DIF: Easy	OBJ: Literary Analysis

Vocabulary and Grammar

14. ANS: B	DIF: Easy	OBJ: Vocabulary
15. ANS: D	DIF: Easy	OBJ: Grammar

Essay

16. Students should recognize Toby's kindness, generosity, knowledge of magic, and willingness to help other slaves escape to freedom and the Overseer's cruelty, use of physical punishment to control the slaves, and willingness to try to prevent the slaves from escaping.
    Difficulty: *Easy*
    Objective: *Essay*

17. Students should recognize that the folk tale depicts the degradation and injustice of slavery as well as the importance of freedom and the importance of not giving up hope for freedom.
    Difficulty: *Easy*
    Objective: *Essay*

Selection Test B, p. 158

Critical Reading

1. ANS: C	DIF: Average	OBJ: Comprehension
2. ANS: C	DIF: Average	OBJ: Interpretation
3. ANS: D	DIF: Average	OBJ: Reading
4. ANS: A	DIF: Average	OBJ: Interpretation
5. ANS: A	DIF: Average	OBJ: Comprehension
6. ANS: D	DIF: Challenging	OBJ: Reading
7. ANS: C	DIF: Average	OBJ: Interpretation

8. ANS: B	DIF: Average	OBJ: Reading
9. ANS: C	DIF: Average	OBJ: Interpretation
10. ANS: D	DIF: Challenging	OBJ: Interpretation
11. ANS: B	DIF: Average	OBJ: Literary Analysis
12. ANS: B	DIF: Average	OBJ: Interpretation
13. ANS: D	DIF: Challenging	OBJ: Literary Analysis
14. ANS: B	DIF: Challenging	OBJ: Literary Analysis
15. ANS: A	DIF: Average	OBJ: Literary Analysis

Vocabulary and Grammar

16. ANS: B	DIF: Average	OBJ: Vocabulary
17. ANS: A	DIF: Average	OBJ: Vocabulary
18. ANS: C	DIF: Challenging	OBJ: Vocabulary
19. ANS: B	DIF: Challenging	OBJ: Grammar

Essay

20. Students should offer a well-reasoned explanation of the purpose of the folk tale—for example, that it gave the people hope by showing them triumphing over their enslavement or that it strengthened the community by maintaining their cultural heritage.
    Difficulty: *Average*
    Objective: *Essay*

21. Students should note that both characters are enslaved and both are among those who could fly. They might point out that Sarah is young whereas Toby is old, and Sarah is a mother whereas Toby is not said to have any family. More important, students may realize that Toby has somehow learned to survive the oppression of the Overseer, whereas Sarah appears to be destroyed by it. Toby also has remembered the magic words that allow him to fly, whereas Sarah has forgotten them. Students may suggest that whereas Toby is a savior of sorts, Sarah is a person worthy of being saved.
    Difficulty: *Challenging*
    Objective: *Essay*

"All Stories Are Anansi's" by Harold Courlander

Vocabulary Warm-up Exercises, p. 162

A. 1. accepted
2. respect
3. offering
4. opinion
5. protect
6. therefore

B. Sample Answers
1. (argument); The <u>argument</u> between two guests ruined the party.
2. (captive); The <u>captive</u> tried to escape, but he got caught.

3. (admit); Peter had to admit that his brother was better looking than he.
4. (used to); I'm used to taking a shortcut through the mall to get home.
5. (soldiers); Some soldiers seem too young to fight in a war.

Reading Warm-up A, p. 163

Sample Answers

1. as a gift from the gods; I *accepted* the invitation to Pam's party.
2. storytelling is just for children; In my *opinion*, children watch too much television.
3. insights into what we as a group admire and fear; Traditional tales teach us about ourselves by *providing* insights into what we as a group admire and fear.
4. (folk stories); *Respect* means "to feel admiration for someone or something."
5. (dying out); I think that our community should *protect* and preserve the old historic section of town, declare it a landmark, and prevent it from being torn down.
6. each listener imagines the world in a personal way; I am good in math and study hard, *therefore*, I always get As in the subject.

Reading Warm-up B, p. 164

Sample Answers

1. (this claim); Some people may *argue* this claim.
2. spiders do keep the insect population in check. *Acknowledge* means "to admit."
3. (used to); I'm *accustomed* to seeing my sister putting on makeup in the morning.
4. cast its small flat web down upon its prey; A synonym for *prisoner* is *captive*.
5. around in the dirt; Spiders are often *prowling* along the walls and ceiling of my house.
6. secretly watching, silently capturing, and steadily devouring the earth's smallest enemies; I've read about the Greek *warriors* who fought over Helen of Troy.

"All Stories Are Anansi's" by Harold Courlander

Reading: Use a Venn Diagram to Compare and Contrast, p. 165

1. *Anansi:* is a spider, wants to own all stories, is deceitful; *Both:* are animals in the same jungle; *Onini:* is a snake, is proud; is trusting
2. *Hornets:* are small, are insects, are taken live to the Sky God; *Both:* are dwellers in the same jungle, trust Anansi, are fooled by Anansi, are captured by Anansi; *Leopard:* is huge, is a mammal, is killed by Anansi

Literary Analysis: Folk Tale, p. 166

Sample Answers

1. The passage shows that storytelling was highly valued.
2. The passage teaches the lesson that it is dangerous to be too trusting.
3. This passage also shows that storytelling was highly valued. OR This passage teaches the lesson that if you work hard to achieve something, you will be rewarded.

Vocabulary Builder, p. 167

A. Sample Answers

1. Yes; *yearned* means "wanted very much," and the hornets surely wanted revenge.
2. A *gourd* would be used as a cup.
3. Yes; I would give credit to Anansi because he is the owner of all stories.

B. Sample answers follow each true or false designation:

1. F; *Yearn* means "to want very much," so you would not yearn for something you did not want.
2. T; A *gourd* can be used to drink from.
3. F; *Acknowledge* means "to recognize," and you cannot recognize someone by ignoring him or her.

C. 1. C; 2. A; 3. C

Enrichment: Making Plans, p. 170

Students should describe a plan for catching each creature—for example, they might suggest putting honey in a jar, waiting for the hornets to fly into it, and putting a lid on the jar. Their plans need not be practical, but their descriptions should demonstrate some understanding of what might be involved in trapping the animals named.

"The People Could Fly" by Virginia Hamilton
"All Stories Are Anansi's" by Harold Courlander

Build Language Skills: Vocabulary, p. 171

A. Sample Answers

1. The story of the family who lost all their possessions in a flood made me sad.
2. Tom took his teacher's advice seriously and immediately began studying harder.

B. Sample answers follow the true or false designations:

1. F; When you *analyze* a problem, you examine something in detail.
2. F; A *characteristic* is a quality that makes something recognizable, and suspense is a quality of most mysteries.
3. T; An *aspect* is a feature of something, and the common character type is a feature of a folk tale.

4. T; A *detail* is a small part of something, and it may or may not be important.

5. F; If something is *unique*, there is nothing else like it.

Build Language Skills: Grammar, p. 172

A.
1. James lives at 115 Elm St., Pleasant Valley, NE.
2. The gardener said that if your yard measures 50 ft. (16.6 yd.) by 40 ft. (13.3 yd.), you will need 2 lbs. of fertilizer.
3. Mr. Raymond works for the UN.

B. Students should write a grammatically correct message that contains at least five correctly formed abbreviations.

"All Stories Are Anansi's" by Harold Courlander

Selection Test A, p. 173

Critical Reading

1. ANS: D	DIF: Easy	OBJ: Literary Analysis
2. ANS: B	DIF: Easy	OBJ: Comprehension
3. ANS: C	DIF: Easy	OBJ: Interpretation
4. ANS: A	DIF: Easy	OBJ: Comprehension
5. ANS: B	DIF: Easy	OBJ: Interpretation
6. ANS: A	DIF: Easy	OBJ: Interpretation
7. ANS: C	DIF: Easy	OBJ: Interpretation
8. ANS: D	DIF: Easy	OBJ: Interpretation
9. ANS: B	DIF: Easy	OBJ: Interpretation
10. ANS: C	DIF: Easy	OBJ: Reading
11. ANS: C	DIF: Easy	OBJ: Reading
12. ANS: A	DIF: Easy	OBJ: Literary Analysis
13. ANS: A	DIF: Easy	OBJ: Literary Analysis

Vocabulary and Grammar

14. ANS: B	DIF: Easy	OBJ: Vocabulary
15. ANS: B	DIF: Easy	OBJ: Grammar

Essay

16. Students who admire Anansi should point out that he is a tiny spider who uses his intelligence to get the better of animals who are bigger, stronger, and more powerful than he; students who do not admire him may point out that Anansi should not be respected because he uses trickery and takes advantage of his victims' weaknesses to get what he wants.
Difficulty: *Easy*
Objective: *Essay*

17. Students' responses should reflect their understanding of Anansi's trick in each case, taking advantage of the hornets' dislike or fear of rain, the python's pride in his length, and the leopard's habit of walking along the ground. Students are likely to choose the hornets' or the python's capture if they are inclined to appreciate

Anansi's verbal skills; they will choose the leopard's capture if they enjoy the physical trickery and the image of a tiny spider causing a leopard to be hung from a tree.
Difficulty: *Easy*
Objective: *Essay*

Selection Test B, p. 176

Critical Reading

1. ANS: C	DIF: Average	OBJ: Literary Analysis
2. ANS: B	DIF: Average	OBJ: Comprehension
3. ANS: D	DIF: Average	OBJ: Comprehension
4. ANS: A	DIF: Challenging	OBJ: Literary Analysis
5. ANS: A	DIF: Average	OBJ: Interpretation
6. ANS: D	DIF: Average	OBJ: Reading
7. ANS: C	DIF: Average	OBJ: Reading
8. ANS: D	DIF: Average	OBJ: Interpretation
9. ANS: B	DIF: Challenging	OBJ: Literary Analysis
10. ANS: C	DIF: Average	OBJ: Reading
11. ANS: D	DIF: Average	OBJ: Literary Analysis
12. ANS: B	DIF: Challenging	OBJ: Interpretation
13. ANS: A	DIF: Challenging	OBJ: Interpretation
14. ANS: A	DIF: Average	OBJ: Reading

Vocabulary and Grammar

15. ANS: A	DIF: Average	OBJ: Vocabulary
16. ANS: C	DIF: Average	OBJ: Vocabulary
17. ANS: D	DIF: Average	OBJ: Grammar
18. ANS: C	DIF: Challenging	OBJ: Grammar

Essay

19. Students may argue that Anansi is simply out to prove that he is craftier than the most powerful families, the great warriors, and the great chiefs. Alternatively, they may point out that storytelling must have been highly prized by the people who told this tale, and Anansi wants the everlasting glory that his achievement wins for him: Everyone who tells a story from then on must acknowledge that the story belongs to Anansi.
Difficulty: *Average*
Objective: *Essay*

20. Among the elements that students might mention are these: The Africans who told "All Stories Are Anansi's" lived in a forest and were very familiar with the habits of wild animals; they valued intelligence and enjoyed the exploits of trickster characters; they respected small creatures that are able to defeat those who are stronger and more powerful than they; they prized the tradition of storytelling; they taught their children that naivete and foolishness are potentially dangerous character traits.
Difficulty: *Challenging*
Objective: *Essay*

"The Fox Outwits the Crow" by William Cleary
"The Fox and the Crow" by Aesop

Vocabulary Warm-up Exercises, p. 180

A. 1. whiff
2. curves
3. figure
4. snatched
5. trust
6. fondly

B. Sample Answers

1. The most <u>glamorous</u> thing I have ever done is ride in a convertible with the top down.
2. I would never act out of <u>malice</u> toward a friend because I value the friendship and would never want to hurt someone I care about.
3. I <u>exchange</u> cards and sometimes gifts with my friends on Valentine's Day.
4. People like stories with a <u>moral</u> because that lesson can usually be applied to something in their daily lives.
5. My <u>advice</u> to that person would be "Shop around until you find the best value for your money!"

Reading Warm-up A, p. 181

Sample Answers

1. (lovingly); She *fondly* kissed her mother goodbye.
2. <u>of her body</u>; *Curves* are round, bending lines.
3. (of a man); Mira turned and saw the *shape* of a man wearing clothes of purple satin and a peacock-feathered hat.
4. <u>his perfume</u>; Sometimes I get a *whiff* of the fresh coffee my mom is making in the morning.
5. (Vanity); I *trust* my dad because he is smart and honest.
6. (mirror); Jack *grabbed* hold of the Golden Goose and raced down the ladder with the Giant behind him.

Reading Warm-up B, p. 182

Sample Answers

1. (many tropical birds); I think movie stars are *glamorous*.
2. <u>bits of food</u>; *Exchange* means "trade one thing for another."
3. <u>acts of evil intent</u>; The evil alien in the sci-fi movie looked at his victim with *malice*.
4. (false words); People use *flattery* to trick other people into giving them something they want.
5. (lesson); I like the *moral* that says, "Don't count your chickens before they hatch!" which to me means, "Don't expect things that might not happen."
6. (from spirits); My friend always asks for my *advice*, but she never follows it.

Literary Analysis: Comparing Tone, p. 183

Sample Answers

Note that students may use *serious* instead of *formal* and *informal* instead of *playful*, and vice versa, but not *serious* instead of *playful*, and so on:

1. informal / formal
2. playful / serious
3. playful / formal
4. playful / formal
5. informal / formal
6. informal / formal
7. playful / serious
8. Cleary is amused by his subject and his characters; Aesop treats them respectfully.

Vocabulary Builder, p. 184

A. Sample answers follow the true or false designations:

1. T; A bloodhound's sense of smell is very strong.
2. F; Flatterers are dishonest and insincere.
3. F; Something that is glossy has a smooth, shiny finish.
4. T; Most people would feel ill will toward someone who has harmed them.
5. F; Hors d'oeuvres are served before a main course.
6. T; To exceed expectations, one must do better than expected.

B. 1. D; 2. C; 3. D

Selection Test A, p. 186

Critical Reading

1. ANS: A	DIF: Easy	OBJ: Comprehension
2. ANS: D	DIF: Easy	OBJ: Interpretation
3. ANS: C	DIF: Easy	OBJ: Comprehension
4. ANS: A	DIF: Easy	OBJ: Literary Analysis
5. ANS: D	DIF: Easy	OBJ: Interpretation
6. ANS: C	DIF: Easy	OBJ: Interpretation
7. ANS: B	DIF: Easy	OBJ: Interpretation
8. ANS: B	DIF: Easy	OBJ: Literary Analysis
9. ANS: C	DIF: Easy	OBJ: Interpretation
10. ANS: B	DIF: Easy	OBJ: Literary Analysis
11. ANS: A	DIF: Easy	OBJ: Literary Analysis
12. ANS: C	DIF: Easy	OBJ: Literary Analysis

Vocabulary

13. ANS: D	DIF: Easy	OBJ: Vocabulary
14. ANS: B	DIF: Easy	OBJ: Vocabulary
15. ANS: A	DIF: Easy	OBJ: Vocabulary

Essay

16. Students should recognize that both characters are much the same: both find a piece of cheese; both, because of their vanity, fall victim to the fox's flattery and lose the cheese; both learn that believing in flattery comes at a high price. For differences, students may point to the additional details in "The Fox Outwits the Crow," such as those about opera.

Difficulty: *Easy*

Objective: *Essay*

17. Students should recognize that both characters are similar: Both flatter a crow to get the crow to drop the cheese she is holding in her beak. They differ in the tone of their speech: The Fox in the fable speaks formally; the fox in the poem speaks playfully.

Difficulty: *Easy*

Objective: *Essay*

Selection Test B, p. 189

Critical Reading

1. ANS: C	DIF: Average	OBJ: Comprehension
2. ANS: C	DIF: Challenging	OBJ: Interpretation
3. ANS: A	DIF: Average	OBJ: Literary Analysis
4. ANS: D	DIF: Average	OBJ: Interpretation
5. ANS: D	DIF: Average	OBJ: Interpretation
6. ANS: A	DIF: Average	OBJ: Comprehension
7. ANS: D	DIF: Average	OBJ: Interpretation
8. ANS: B	DIF: Average	OBJ: Literary Analysis
9. ANS: B	DIF: Average	OBJ: Interpretation
10. ANS: C	DIF: Average	OBJ: Interpretation
11. ANS: A	DIF: Challenging	OBJ: Interpretation
12. ANS: A	DIF: Average	OBJ: Literary Analysis
13. ANS: A	DIF: Average	OBJ: Literary Analysis
14. ANS: C	DIF: Average	OBJ: Literary Analysis

Vocabulary

15. ANS: D	DIF: Average	OBJ: Vocabulary
16. ANS: B	DIF: Average	OBJ: Vocabulary
17. ANS: A	DIF: Average	OBJ: Vocabulary

Essay

18. Students should recognize that the crows are similar. Both find a piece of cheese and lose it when they fall victim to the cunning and flattery of a fox. Both are vain, arrogant creatures. Both are advised not to trust a flatterer. In citing differences, students may point to the additional details in "The Flox Outwits the Crow," such as the crow's belief that she is Maria Callas. They should note that the additional details in that selection

make the crow's attitude seem more extreme—she seems more vain and more arrogant than the Crow in "The Fox and the Crow."

Difficulty: *Average*

Objective: *Essay*

19. Students should point to the seriousness and formality of "The Fox and the Crow" and the playfulness and informality of "The Fox Outwits the Crow." They might note that the fox in the poem is more provocative and that the poem includes more details, such as those about opera. Students should recognize that Aesop seems to want only that his readers learn a lesson, whereas Cleary seems to want not just to teach a lesson but to amuse his readers and perhaps impress them with his own cleverness. Students' explanations of the way the tone influenced their attitude should reflect their descriptions of how they thought the writer wanted them to react.

Difficulty: *Challenging*

Objective: *Essay*

Writing Workshop—Unit 6, Part 2

Research Report: Integrating Grammar Skills, p. 193

A. 1. they; 2. her; 3. me; 4. us;

B. 1. Wendell, Terry, and I like to play basketball.

2. Terry's brother taught Wendell and me some good moves.

3. correct

4. He and Terry's brother have been playing together for years.

Spelling Workshop—Unit 6

Greek Roots and Word Families, p. 194

A. 1. symphony; 2. chronological; 3. phonics; 4. disaster; 5. astronomy; 6. chronic; 7. synchronize; 8. astronaut; 9. saxophone; 10. asterisk

B. Answers will vary.

Unit 6, Part 2 Answers

Benchmark Test 12, p. 197

MULTIPLE CHOICE

1. ANS: C

2. ANS: A

3. ANS: A

4. ANS: C

5. ANS: B

6. ANS: D

7. ANS: C

8. ANS: A

9. ANS: D

10. ANS: C

11. ANS: B

12. ANS: D

13. ANS: D

14. ANS: C

15. ANS: A

16. ANS: A

17. ANS: D

18. ANS: B

19. ANS: D

20. ANS: C

21. ANS: D

22. ANS: B

23. ANS: A

24. ANS: C

25. ANS: C

26. ANS: D

27. ANS: A

28. ANS: B

29. ANS: D

30. ANS: C

31. ANS: D

ESSAY

32. Students' summaries should be reasonably short and should focus on main ideas. They should give information on the setting or main settings, the major characters, the main events, the central conflict, and the final outcome of that conflict.

33. Students' reviews should give their opinion of the characters, the plot, and other details in the work. They should support their opinions with details from the work. They should open or conclude with a recommendation about whether or not others should read the tale.

34. Students should identify a subject that is neither too narrow nor too broad. They should list information sources that seem useful for investigating the subject; for example, if their subject is a person, they might list biographical references; if their subject is a place, they might list an atlas or book of maps.

CURRICULUM